CW00542991

Reading

1 **a** Read the article quickly and tick the best summary (1–3).

1 It tells the story of Susan Boyle's life and rise to stardom as a singer. ☐

2 It argues that we shouldn't judge people until we get to know them. ☐

3 It uses the story of Susan Boyle to show that we often judge people by appearances. ☐

b Find the words and phrases from the box in the article and match them with the definitions (1–12).

> solely   instant   tendency   bemused
> self-deluded   wannabe   gasp   homely   soaring
> standing ovation   dichotomy   prodigious

1 difference between two things or ideas _____
2 somebody who would like to be a star _____
3 having a false impression of one's own talent _____
4 a short sudden noise when you breathe in _____
5 rising, getting higher and higher _____
6 only, exclusively _____
7 ordinary-looking, not very attractive _____
8 showing approval of a performance by standing up and applauding _____
9 immediate _____
10 likelihood, something which often happens _____
11 rare, unusual, very talented _____
12 slightly confused, unable to understand _____

c Read the article again and answer the questions (1–8).

1 What is the 'well-known saying' referred to in the first paragraph?

_____

2 Why do scientists think judging by appearances was necessary for early humans?

_____

3 Where is Susan Boyle from?

_____

4 What was watched 200 million times on YouTube?

_____

5 How was Susan Boyle different from the usual contestants on *Britain's Got Talent*?

_____

6 What was the audience's first impression of Susan Boyle?

_____

7 What made the audience change its opinion of Susan?

_____

8 According to the article, what does Susan Boyle's story prove?

_____

Don't judge a book by its cover

Most people agree with this well-known saying but few follow its advice. For the truth is that, whether we like it or not, our brains are programmed to make immediate judgements based almost solely on first impressions. Scientists argue that this is a survival mechanism which dates from humanity's early history – a time when the world was full of danger and it was necessary for people to make instant life-or-death decisions.

The strength of our tendency to judge by appearances has recently been illustrated by the incredible story of Susan Boyle, an unemployed Scottish woman who shot to international stardom after appearing on a TV talent show. Her appearance on the show became one of the most popular videos on YouTube, with more than 200 million viewings. Her debut CD sold more than 9 million copies within six weeks of its release.

In fact, Boyle's appearance on *Britain's Got Talent* was one of the most memorable and surprising moments in recent TV history. Most of the performers on the talent show are young hopefuls. Some have talent but many are simply good-looking youngsters who dream of becoming pop stars but have no musical ability or background. On one particular show, a rather plain, middle-aged woman with an unflattering hairstyle and an old-fashioned dress appeared on stage.

If you watch the YouTube clip, you will see what happens next …

The audience looks bemused – what is someone like this doing on a show where most contestants are in their teens or early 20s? In a strong Scottish accent, the woman tells the judges that her name is Susan, she comes from a small village near Glasgow, she's 47, and wants to become a professional singer. The audience prepares itself for an embarrassing display by another self-deluded wannabe. What hope does someone like this have of becoming a star?

Then Susan opens her mouth and begins to sing. A gasp of amazement goes up from the audience, for the contrast between her homely appearance and powerful soaring voice is almost overpowering. They begin to clap and scream. Within a few moments, most of the audience are on their feet, giving Susan Boyle a standing ovation.

For many viewers, it was the unexpected dichotomy between Boyle's physical appearance and her prodigious talent that was so memorable. But why should it be such a shock that someone like Susan Boyle can have a wonderful and rare talent? The truth is, however sophisticated we believe we are, we still make instant judgements based purely on outward appearances. If someone doesn't look beautiful, we still find it difficult to believe that they can have a beautiful voice.

Grammar | overview (1): the present and future

2 Complete the sentences using appropriate forms of the words in brackets.

1 I'm not sure, but I think I _____ the salad. (try)
2 We're so excited about our holiday – we _____ the Taj Mahal! (see)
3 Some form of life _____ even in the deepest parts of the ocean. (exist)
4 I _____ my husband's car this week because mine is at the garage. (use)
5 Peter hates buses so he _____ by car. (probably / come)
6 The company _____ the factory for a month every August. (close)
7 Look at those dark clouds, I think there _____ a storm. (be)
8 We _____ our grandmother every Sunday. (visit)
9 Don't disturb me – I _____ the news. (watch)
10 Look in the bottom drawer; that's where we _____ our insurance documents. (keep)
11 I can't see you next Tuesday because I _____ a conference. (attend)
12 We haven't set an exact date, but the wedding _____ sometime in the spring. (definitely / be)

Vocabulary | ways of speaking

3 Use the clues to complete the crossword.

1 People _____ each other differently in different cultures.
2 You really shouldn't _____ about other people behind their backs.
3 I can hardly hear you – could you _____ up?
4 When I'm nervous I often _____ over my words.
5 Everyone enjoys being given a _____ .
6 Let's have a _____ about it tomorrow.
7 Parties can make you nervous if you're not good at _____ talk.
8 I can't stand people who _____ about how much money they've got.
9 Don't _____ . I can't hear what you're saying.

How to... | make a good first impression

4 Complete the dialogue with words and phrases from the box.

> a pleasure   are you   do you do
> have you lived here long
> I know what you mean   pleased
> really nice talking   really
> sounds interesting   when did you move in

A: Hi. I'm Karl, your new neighbour.
B: (1) _____ to meet you. My name's Sophie.
A: It's (2) _____ to meet you too. It's so important to know your neighbours, don't you think?
B: Absolutely. (3) _____ ?
A: Just a few days ago.
B: Well, it's a lovely area.
A: I know. (4) _____ ?
B: Oh, yes. Ten years.
A: (5) _____ ?
B: Yes. I moved here when I got a job at the university.
A: That (6) _____ .
B: Yes, I really enjoy working there. What (7) _____ ?
A: I'm a social worker.
B: (8) _____ ? That must be a fascinating job!
A: Sometimes, but I have to deal with people with serious problems so it can also be quite stressful.
B: (9) _____ . But I suppose it's nice to know you are helping people.
A: Yes, it's satisfying.
B: Well, it's been (10) _____ to you. You should come over for coffee at the weekend and I can tell you all about our other neighbours.
A: That would be great ...

Listening

1 **a** 2 Cover the audioscript. Listen to a radio programme and choose the best summary (1–3).

1 The recent history of juggling

2 Different types of juggling around the world

3 Juggling in ancient times

b Listen again and write true (T) or false (F).

1 David Stourton is a juggler. ☐

2 Professional jugglers use the term 'toss juggling'. ☐

3 The earliest picture of jugglers is from ancient China. ☐

4 There is a picture of Egyptian jugglers in a museum in Berlin. ☐

5 There is no evidence of juggling in the Americas. ☐

6 Tagatus Ursus was a Roman juggler. ☐

7 There were probably jugglers in Ireland in ancient times. ☐

8 Jugglers were usually also clowns or jesters. ☐

c Now read the audioscript and match words with the definitions (1–8).

1 writer of a particular book _____

2 throwing _____

3 a building where someone is buried _____

4 metal weapons with sharp blades _____

5 restricted to one area _____

6 something that shows where somebody is buried (two words) _____

7 spoken stories about the ancient past _____

8 connected _____

AUDIOSCRIPT

Woman: On today's *Meet the Author* we're talking to David Stourton, author of *A Short History of Juggling*. David, welcome to the programme.

David: Thanks.

Woman: Now, I suppose we all have a broad idea of what juggling is, but could you tell us what you mean by 'juggling'?

David: Sure. I pretty much stuck to the traditional idea of juggling. I think the dictionary calls it 'keeping two or more objects in the air at one time by alternately tossing and catching them'. In the profession, we call that 'toss juggling'. I think that's the type of juggling most people are familiar with.

Woman: Has juggling been around for a long time?

David: Oh yes. I found references to juggling from more than 3,000 years ago. There are some Egyptian tomb paintings which show jugglers from the Middle Kingdom period and there's an ancient Egyptian statue of a juggler in the Staatliche museum in Berlin.

Woman: What about written records?

David: Well, the earliest written record that we know of is from ancient China. There's a book from the 3rd or 4th century BC which describes a juggler who could throw seven swords in the air.

Woman: That sounds like something from one of those Chinese martial arts movies!

David: Yes, juggling with swords is a well-established tradition in the Far East.

Woman: So was juggling confined to the Middle East and Asia in ancient times?

David: Not at all. There were lots of jugglers in ancient Rome. We even know the name of one of them – Tagatus Ursus.

Woman: Did the Romans juggle with knives, like the Chinese?

David: Probably not. We know that Tagatus Ursus juggled glass balls, because they're specifically mentioned on his grave stone. And, interestingly, when the Spanish discovered the Americas, they noted in their reports and diaries that the Aztecs had jugglers.

Woman: Are there any records of juggling here in Britain?

David: Well, not exactly, but jugglers are mentioned in several of the Irish and Norse myths, which date from the 5th to the 12th centuries. Of course, by the time of the Middle Ages, there are plenty of references to jugglers in Britain.

Woman: You talk about jugglers as if they were part of an actual profession. I mean, is that really the case?

David: It's hard to say with any certainty. In some cases, jugglers were also clowns or jesters, or even acrobats.

Woman: Yes, I can see how the skills might be linked. Now, can you tell us about the more recent history of juggling ... ?

Grammar | overview (2): the past

2 Complete the sentences using an appropriate form of verbs from the box.

> drink go lose eat meet rain pass
> release revise watch

1 David _____ an apple when he broke a tooth.
2 We were very excited because we _____ to Disneyland before.
3 I finally _____ my driving test after three attempts!
4 The weather was terrible. In fact, it _____ on the day we arrived and on the day we left!
5 When I opened the fridge, I found that my flatmate _____ all the milk!
6 The film *Avatar* _____ in 2010.
7 I arrived home and saw my husband waiting outside the door – he _____ his key!
8 My mother _____ my father at a nightclub in 1990.
9 We _____ TV when the lights suddenly went out.
10 I stayed at home most evenings while I _____ for my exams.

3 Find the mistakes in four of these sentences and correct them.

1 That restaurant's great – I had been there last month.
2 It was a lovely morning. The sun was shining and the birds were singing.
3 I was phoning you three times. Where were you?
4 The doorbell rang while I had a shower.
5 Juan broke his leg in a motorbike accident last week.
6 It was our first visit – we weren't going there before.

Vocabulary | making adjectives from nouns

4 Complete the missing word in each sentence.

1 My nephew's very a_____c. He loves painting.
2 I am r_____e for our after-sales service.
3 Ice-skating well requires great s_____l.
4 J_____y is often known as 'the little green monster'.
5 Dorotea runs a very s_____l business.
6 People in big cities are often more l_____y than people in small towns.
7 I've got very big feet so I often get f_____d when I'm trying to buy shoes.
8 Albert Einstein was famous for his incredible i_____t.

How to... | manage a conversation

5 🔘 3 Listen to the dialogue and match the <u>underlined</u> expressions (1–6) with the explanations (a–f).

A: So, have you booked your holiday yet?
B: No. We're finding it hard to decide what to do.
A: (1) <u>Yes, it's a difficult decision, isn't it?</u>
B: We were thinking about Florida. (2) <u>Have you been there?</u>
A: Yes, we've been to Miami a couple of times.
B: (3) <u>So, you know it quite well then?</u>
A: I wouldn't say that exactly.
B: I've heard the beaches are lovely.
A: They are. And the sea's warm and calm – perfect for swimming.
B: (4) <u>That's not the experience I've had. We went to Cuba a few years ago and the sea was quite rough.</u> And I know that's not far from Miami.
A: (5) <u>Yes. I suppose it depends on the time of year. During the hurricane season the waves can be pretty enormous.</u>
B: (6) <u>I suppose you're right. We went in October and I think that's when they often get hurricanes.</u>

a ask a direct question ☐
b reformulate someone's answer into another question ☐
c comment on someone's point and back up with your own example ☐
d refer to someone's point and back up with your own example ☐
e agree with someone's point ☐
f find similarities with someone else's point ☐

Pronunciation | sounding tentative

6 **a** 🔘 4 Listen to the sentences (1–4) from exercise 5. Write T (tentative) or C (more confident).

1 I wouldn't say that exactly. ☐
2 That's not the experience I've had. ☐
3 The sea's warm and calm – perfect for swimming. ☐
4 Yes, I suppose it depends on the time of year. ☐

b Listen again and repeat the sentences.

Listening

1 **a** 🔵 5 Cover the audioscript. Listen to the dialogues (1–4) and match them with the situations (a–d).

a on a train ☐
b in a shop ☐
c a survey ☐
d in a café ☐

b The following statements all contain a mistake. Listen again and correct the mistakes.

Dialogue 1

1 The man only uses his phone to send text messages.

2 He's able to use his phone at work.

Dialogue 2

3 The man enjoys hearing people on the phone when he's on the train.

4 The woman thinks it's always expensive to make mobile calls.

Dialogue 3

5 Steve's mobile was expensive.

6 John doesn't think Steve's new phone is very good.

Dialogue 4

7 The customer doesn't have any children.

8 If he isn't happy after ten days, the customer can get a different phone.

c Now read the audioscript. Find the words and phrases from the box and match them with the meanings (1–9).

> non-stop   drives me mad   cost a bomb   tariffs
> on special offer   tracks   the really neat thing
> loads   keep in touch

1 for sale at a reduced price _____
2 maintain contact with someone when you are physically separated _____
3 songs or short pieces of music _____
4 a large quantity _____
5 all the time _____
6 prices for using a service _____
7 makes me very angry _____
8 very expensive _____
9 something particularly impressive _____

AUDIOSCRIPT

Dialogue 1

A: Excuse me. We're doing a survey on mobile phones. Could I ask you a few questions?

B: Sure.

A: Do you own a mobile phone?

B: Yes.

A: And what do you mainly use it for?

B: Sending text messages, I suppose.

A: How many would you send on an average day?

B: Well, about five or six usually.

A: And are those mainly for business or social purposes?

B: Oh, just social. I can't use my phone at work – I'm an airline pilot.

Dialogue 2

A: Honestly. You want some peace and quiet and all you hear is those awful mobile phones non-stop. It drives me mad!

B: Yeah, and people talk such rubbish, don't they? 'Er, I'm on the train, and now we're pulling in at a station.'

A: It must cost a bomb to make all those calls.

B: Maybe they're on one of those 'cheap daytime calls' tariffs.

Dialogue 3

A: Is that a new mobile, Steve?

B: Yeah. I got it on special offer.

A: It looks very sophisticated.

B: Mm. It was really good value. It's got a camera and it can play MP3 files.

A: So you can listen to all the latest tracks.

B: Exactly. But the really neat thing is that it's got this special text-messaging service that gives you all the latest football results. You should get one, John. They had loads of them in stock.

Dialogue 4

A: Which model are you interested in, sir?

B: Well, I'm not sure. But I want a phone that takes photos.

A: OK. Most of them do that now, anyway.

B: Oh, right. Well, I like to keep in touch with the kids when I'm abroad, so I need a phone that works in other countries.

A: In that case, you need a 'triband' phone then. Anything else?

B: Yes, I want something that's really small and light, you know, easy to carry around.

A: Well, what about this Minirola? We have a ten-day trial period policy here. If you're not happy with it, you could bring it back and we'll return your money.

4 Find the mistakes in five of these sentences and correct them.

1 You have get a visa to work in the US.

2 We didn't had to pay cash because the hotel accepted credit cards.

3 You mustn't use mobile phones during the flight.

4 Carlos got lost – we should given him a map.

5 I failed the exam so I have to take it again next year.

6 You should always to wash your hands before eating.

7 In those days people could drive a car without having a licence.

8 Is it true that you can seeing the Great Wall of China from space?

Pronunciation | connected speech (1)

5 a Look at the underlined words (1–10) in the dialogues and tick (✓) the weak forms.

Dialogue 1

A: (1) Could I ask you a few questions?

B: Sure.

A: Do you own a mobile phone?

Dialogue 2

A: It was really good value. It's got a camera and it (2) can play MP3 files.

B: So you (3) can listen to all the latest tracks?

Dialogue 3

A: Could you give me some advice?

B: Yes. Of course I (4) can.

A: Do you think I should (5) have spoken to Laura yesterday?

B: I don't know. But you'll have (6) to speak to her sometime.

Dialogue 4

A: What happened at the shop?

B: Oh, it was fine. I (7) was able (8) to get a refund.

A: Did you have (9) to show them the receipt.

B: No, luckily I didn't have (10) to.

b 🌐 6 Listen and check the pronunciation. Then repeat the sentences.

Vocabulary | keeping in touch

2 Read the pairs of sentences. Write S (same meaning) or D (different meaning).

1 a Remember to keep in touch.
  b Don't forget to phone me while you're away. ☐

2 a I've lost touch with my schoolfriends.
  b I don't see my schoolfriends very often. ☐

3 a We can touch base tomorrow.
  b Let's spend the day together tomorrow. ☐

4 a She'll be out of touch for a few days.
  b She's going to stay in a place with no phone signal or Internet access. ☐

5 a Will you get in touch with the plumber?
  b Are you going to contact the plumber? ☐

Grammar | obligation and ability

3 Choose the correct words in *italics*. In two cases both are correct.

1 You *mustn't/don't have to* bring any money – everything's included in the price.

2 The receptionist told me I wasn't smartly dressed enough, but I *was able to/could* persuade her to let me in anyway.

3 You *mustn't/shouldn't* have spoken to him like that – he was only doing his job!

4 The service was excellent; I think you *must/should* give the waiter a big tip.

5 Although we *should have got/had to get* tickets in advance, they weren't too expensive.

6 This is a hospital – you *don't have to/mustn't* smoke in here!

7 I can't believe you gave up so easily – you *had to try/should have tried* harder!

8 When I was younger I *could/was able to* run for miles without getting tired.

9 Luckily for us, we *shouldn't have paid/ didn't have to pay* extra for seats in the front row.

10 All applicants *have to/must* provide identification and proof of address.

Review and consolidation unit 1

The present and future

1 Complete the dialogue with forms of words from the box.

> ask   be   get   live   meet   repair   she   stay   take
> you catch   you leave

Ana: (1) _____ so soon? You've only just arrived!

Luis: I know, but I (2) _____ Helena at one o'clock.

Ana: Oh. How (3) _____ she?

Luis: Not too bad. She (4) _____ better but her leg is still in a plaster cast!

Ana: How long (5) _____ in plaster?

Luis: I'm not sure, but I think they (6) _____ it off in the next week or two.

Ana: That's not too bad, I suppose. Is there anything I can do for her?

Luis: Like what?

Ana: I know she (7) _____ a long way from the shops – I could help her with the shopping.

Luis: That's a nice idea. I (8) _____ her when I see her later.

Ana: Well, it was lovely to see you again.
(9) _____ the bus back to town?

Luis: No, I've got my motorbike.

Ana: Right. Well make sure you take the by-pass on your way back. They (10) _____ the bridge so the main road is closed at the moment.

The past

2 Complete the sentences using suitable forms of the words in brackets.

1   I _____ (meet) my girlfriend while I _____ (work) as a waiter in Prague in 2009.

2   After the show last night we _____ (drive) to a nice restaurant and _____ (have) a delicious supper.

3   I wanted to go to the art exhibition because I _____ (not see) any of Picasso's paintings before.

4   We _____ (miss) the train because when we _____ (get) to the station it _____ (already leave).

5   When we _____ (arrive) at the beach it was really hot and the sun _____ (shine) – so we _____ (take off) our clothes and _____ (run) into the sea.

6   I _____ (make) a terrible mistake yesterday – when I _____ (get) to the airport I realised I _____ (leave) my passport at home!

7   Most of the inhabitants _____ (sleep) when the first earthquake _____ (strike) the town.

8   I showed the children a DVD of *The Lion King*, but they _____ (see) the film so often that they _____ (know) all the songs by heart and they _____ (find) it a bit boring.

Obligation and ability

3 Read all the sentence endings and choose possible (✓) or not possible (✗) for each. Think about meaning and grammar.

1   It's a very formal restaurant so …
   a   you have to wear a tie.   ☐
   b   you should wear a tie.   ☐
   c   you don't have to wear informal clothes.   ☐

2   My computer broke down but luckily …
   a   Carla had been able to fix it.   ☐
   b   I can repair it yesterday.   ☐
   c   he was able to repair it for me.   ☐

3   The train was completely full and all the seats were taken so …
   a   we didn't have to stand up.   ☐
   b   we had to stand up for the whole journey.   ☐
   c   we should have stood up for most of the journey.   ☐

4   My uncle offered us a lift so …
   a   we didn't have to get a taxi.   ☐
   b   we should have caught the bus.   ☐
   c   we had to go by taxi.   ☐

5   This is a food preparation area so …
   a   you mustn't smoke in here.   ☐
   b   you don't have to smoke here.   ☐
   c   you shouldn't smoke here.   ☐

How to…

4 Match the expressions (1–6) with the descriptions (a–f).

1   Really? And then what happened?

2   I really must go. But it was great to meet you.

3   Nice to meet you too.

4   So, you must know this area well?

5   How long have you been a student here?

6   That's quite right.

a   Ask a direct question

b   Reformulate someone's answer into another question

c   Finish a conversation politely

d   Agree with someone's point

e   Sound interested in the other person

f   Respond to a greeting

Family/relationships

5 Use the clues to complete the crossword.

1 John's ____ divorced him after they'd been married for ten years.
2 She isn't married but she's got a ____.
3 I don't know him well. He's only an ____.
4 He's an old friend – we are very ____.
5 Clare's a ____ of mine – we both work in the travel agency.
6 She's perfect for you. I'm sure you'll ____ with her.
7 I've got two ____ sisters from my mother's previous marriage.
8 He made a good ____ on his new boss.
9 I prefer to discuss problems face to ____.
10 We're inseparable – I feel he's my real ____.
11 I don't see eye to ____ with my sister.
12 He's the son of my mother's new husband. He's my ____-brother.

Phrasal verbs (relationships)

6 Complete the second sentence so that it has the same meaning as the first, using the correct forms of phrasal verbs from the box.

> bring up   fall out   get on   go out with   look up to
> show off   split up   take after

1 Brenda and Lucy have a good relationship.
  Brenda _____ with Lucy.
2 I've always admired my grandmother.
  I've always _____ my grandmother.
3 It can't be easy raising three children on your own.
  _____ three children on your own can't be easy.
4 Michael and Jane have ended their relationship.
  Michael and Jane _____ .
5 Why does your brother try to impress us all the time?
  Why does your brother _____ all the time?
6 Surinda looks just like her mother.
  Surinda _____ her mother.

7 I've had an argument with my best friend and I'm not speaking to him any more.
  I _____ with my best friend.
8 Henry's having a relationship with one of the girls in his office.
  Henry _____ one of the girls in his office.

Adjectives/nouns

7 Complete the blog using adjectives or nouns from the box. Four of the words are not needed.

> artistic   importance
> important   intellectual
> jealous   loneliness   lonely
> responsibility   responsible
> skill   success   successful

I come from quite a large family. The great thing about a large family is that you never feel (1) _____ because there's always someone to talk to.

My elder brother, James, is a university professor. He's very (2) _____ – his hobby is reading Greek philosophy! I'm the (3) _____ one in the family. I'm a graphic designer. My twin brother, Martin, is the practical one. He's a carpenter and he can do amazing things with wood. It's a (4) _____ I really admire.

But my younger sister, Kate, is the most (5) _____ of us all – she's the managing director of a huge company. She has the ultimate (6) _____ for more than 250 workers. Of course, she earns an enormous salary which we are all a little (7) _____ of! But in the end money doesn't matter. The (8) _____ thing is that we all support each other.

Reading

1 **a** Read the newspaper article quickly and choose the best title.

1 Chinese Motorways

2 Speed Tourists

3 Europe's New Destination

b Read the article again. Write the questions for these answers.

1 seven years

_____
_____

2 120,000

_____
_____

3 speed

_____
_____

4 8,000

_____
_____

5 a Mercedes, an Audi or a BMW

_____
_____

6 240

_____
_____

7 €3,000

_____
_____

8 600

_____
_____

c Match the descriptions (1–6) to words or phrases from the article.

1 two more nouns that mean *tourists*
_____ , _____

2 two more nouns that mean *roads*
_____ , _____

3 another expression that means *travel companies* _____

4 an adverb that means *almost*
_____

5 an adjective that means *like something from a story or legend* _____

6 an -ed adjective that means the opposite of *put off/discouraged*
_____

(1) For years, tourists (1) _____ to Europe to enjoy its many attractions. From the beaches of the Mediterranean to the castles of Scotland, Europe has something for every kind of holidaymaker to enjoy. Now travel agents (2) _____ a new and rather unexpected attraction to the list – the German motorway system. For the last seven years, travel companies (3) _____ Chinese tourists to Germany to experience the thrill of driving on its 'autobahns'. This year more than 120,000 are expected to arrive.

(2) What is it about Germany's autobahns that tempts tourists to travel from halfway across the world? The answer is simple – speed. More than 8,000 kilometres of German motorways have no speed limit – something which is virtually unique in the modern world. Few Europeans realise that Germany's superb roads have an almost mythical reputation in Asia, where highways are often overcrowded, poorly maintained and full of potholes.

(3) Tour operators (4) _____ that offering a Mercedes, an Audi or a BMW capable of 240 kilometres per hour to holidaymakers is the best way of bringing in much-needed foreign exchange.

For the last few years the Chinese economy (5) _____ rapidly and as a result there are plenty of Chinese travellers wealthy enough to afford the €3,000 charged for a six-day 'autobahn tour'. The prices they are charging may seem high, but the 'speed tourists' claim that the thrill of driving at speeds which would almost certainly lead to prison sentences back at home far outweighs the expense involved.

(4) But this new form of tourism (6) _____ so popular with the locals. German road-safety groups (7) _____ negatively to the arrival of the Chinese speed tourists. Figures published by the World Health Organisation show that more than 600 people die on China's roads every day. Even taking into consideration the huge population of China, this is still a horrifying statistic. But the Chinese drivers are undeterred, pointing out that since they first started coming seven years ago, there (8) _____ no major accidents involving speed tourists.

Grammar | Present Perfect Simple and Continuous

2 Complete the gaps in the article (1–8) using Present Perfect Simple or Continuous forms of the verbs from the box. You may need to use negative or passive forms.

> add   be   bring   discover   expand   flock
> prove   react

3 Make responses from the prompts using appropriate forms of the Present Perfect Simple or Continuous and any other necessary words.

Why are you so red?

I / lie / sun / all morning

I've been lying in the sun all morning.

1   Can we go back to the car now?

No / I / not pay / shopping / yet

_____

2   Why are the children soaking wet?

They / swim / the lake

_____

3   Have you tried that new French restaurant yet?

No / never / go / there

_____

4   Michael looks tanned.

Yes / he / just / come back / Miami Beach

_____

5   Why aren't you having any pudding?

I / follow / strict diet / for / last two months

_____

6   Shall I feed the cats?

No / I / already / do / it

_____

7   Is Maria still working on that report?

Yes / she / type / it / lunchtime

_____

8   You're a good teacher and you seem very experienced.

Yes / teach / karate / more than / ten years

_____

9   You look exhausted.

I / wash / the floors / all afternoon

_____

10 Do you still go to the tennis club?

No / I / not be / member / 2010

_____

Pronunciation | connected speech (2)

4 a Look at the underlined words (1–8) then tick (✓) which ones would be said with a weak form.

A: (1) Have you ever (2) been (3) to Paris?

B: Yes, I (4) have.

A: What (5) was it like?

B: It (6) was expensive!

A: (7) Was it? I'm surprised (8) to hear that!

b 🌐 7 Listen and check your answers. Then repeat the sentences.

Vocabulary | describing situations and feelings

5 Complete the summaries using adjectives from the box.

> annoyed   annoying   daunted   daunting
> fascinated   fascinating   inspired   inspiring
> petrified   petrifying

1   **David:** After listening to her speech, I decided to become a doctor.

Her speech was _____ .

David felt _____ by the speech.

2   **Miranda:** Daniel's behaviour made me very angry.

Miranda feels _____ .

Daniel's behaviour was _____ .

3   **Mary:** I thought the exhibition was incredibly interesting.

The exhibition was _____ .

Mary was _____ by the exhibition.

4   **José:** That was the scariest film I've ever seen. I've never been so scared!

José was _____ by the film.

The film was _____ .

5   **Eloise:** I know the job is quite difficult, but that hasn't put me off doing it.

Eloise doesn't think the job is _____ .

She isn't _____ by the job.

Reading

1 **a** Read the webpage and match the headings (a–g) with the paragraphs (1–5). Two headings are not needed.

a Facilities ☐
b Reservations ☐
c Location ☐
d Lapland ☐
e History ☐
f The Ice Hotel ☐
g Construction ☐

b Read the webpage again. Write true (T) or false (F).

1 The Ice Hotel isn't the sort of building that people expect to find in a northern country. ☐
2 People in Jukkasjärvi don't speak Swedish. ☐
3 It takes two days to build the hotel. ☐
4 The hotel is mainly built of ice. ☐
5 A French artist built the first Ice Hotel. ☐
6 Guests sometimes worry about the cold temperatures. ☐
7 Guests can watch films. ☐
8 Visitors can hunt reindeer in the daytime. ☐

c The adverb–adjective collocation *heavily insulated* appears in paragraph 1. <u>Underline</u> one more example in each paragraph.

Unusual Destinations # 22

1 People often choose to have holidays in strange and unusual places. But there can be few places stranger than the Ice Hotel in Sweden, which is visited by almost 37,000 people each winter. Built of snow and ice, the hotel is the very opposite of the <u>heavily insulated</u>, centrally heated buildings. we normally associate with northern countries. Rather than insulate itself from the cold subzero environment all around it, the hotel embraces the wintry surroundings and makes them into part of its attraction.

2 The Ice Hotel is situated in the small village of Jukkasjärvi, next to the river Tornealven. Jukkasjärvi lies 200 kilometres north of the Arctic Circle in Saamiland (the region which used to be known as Lapland), the most northerly part of Sweden. Before the arrival of the Ice Hotel there were almost no tourists in this sparsely populated region, where the local people speak Saami, not Swedish, and there is no industry or pollution.

3 The Ice Hotel is not a permanent building but is rebuilt each winter. Construction of the 5,000 square metre building starts in late October when special snow cannons shoot tons of snow onto steel sections. After two days the steel sections are removed leaving solid snow arches five or six metres wide. Over the following weeks the sections are reused to make more arches. Huge ice blocks are carved from the frozen river to make walls and pillars. About 30,000 tons of snow and 10,000 tons of ice are used to create the solidly built hotel.

4 The story of the Ice Hotel began in the winter of 1989–90. There was an exhibition of ice art in the local village and a cylinder-shaped igloo made of ice was built for the exhibition by well known French artist Jannot Derid. Some of the visitors decided to sleep on reindeer skins in the igloo and found it a relaxing and stimulating experience. Yngve Bergqvist, the owner of the small local inn, realised that others might want to share this unique environment and the concept of the Ice Hotel was born.

5 Visitors to the Ice Hotel are sometimes nervous about staying in a place where the outside temperature in winter is often minus 40 degrees Centigrade. But of course local people have been living in this environment for thousands of years, and conditions inside the Ice Hotel are reasonably comfortable. The temperature is usually around minus four degrees, and guests are provided with thick sleeping bags and their beds are lined with reindeer skins. To keep visitors amused in the evenings the hotel includes an 'ice cinema' and a well stocked 'ice bar'. During the day the hotel company organises sports activities such as white water-rafting, dog-sledding and fishing, and there are tours of local villages and 'safaris' to observe reindeer in their natural habitat.

Vocabulary | weather

2 Use the clues to complete the crossword.

Across

1 very hot
5 light rain
7 no clouds
8 movement of the rain
10 rain from time to time

Down

2 grey sky
3 never the same
4 a light wind
6 adjective from clue 4
7 not warm or very cold
9 quite cold

Pronunciation | connected speech: linking sounds

3 **a** Read the sentences (1–8). Write the linking sound you hear between the underlined words (/w/, /j/ or /r/).

1 My mother is a doctor. _____
2 Who are those people outside? _____
3 Do you want to play another game? _____
4 I wasn't happy about their decision. _____
5 I prefer economics to sociology. _____
6 Is it true you aren't taking the exam? _____
7 My MP3 player is on top of the table. _____
8 We aren't going to the party after all. _____

b 🔘 8 Listen and check. Then repeat the sentences.

Grammar | questions

4 Put the words in the correct order to make questions.

get / when / a / refund / me / Can / you /tell / I'll / ?
Can you tell me when I'll get a refund?

1 to / was / Who / talking / she / ?
_____

2 if / my / Do / know / you / this / seat / is / ?
_____

3 much / costs / it / Can / tell / you / me / how / ?
_____

4 they / car / Where / the / did / take / ?
_____

5 ask / to / the / open / Could / I / you / window / ?
_____

6 the / How / you / computer / do / turn / off / ?
_____

7 correct / Are / the / answers / these / ?
_____

8 been / How / you / here / long / have / working / ?
_____

5 Write indirect questions starting with the words given.

Where are you from?
Can you tell me where you are from?

1 What's your email address?
Can you _____

2 Does Graham Randall live here?
Could I _____

3 Is this the correct platform for the train to Brighton?
Do you _____

4 Which seats in the plane have the most legroom?
I'd like to _____

5 Is the doctor available now?
Can I _____

6 Where exactly does she live?
Can you explain _____

7 How much do the tickets cost?
Do you _____

8 Who is in charge?
Would you tell _____

Listening

1 **a** 🌐 9 Cover the audioscript. Listen to five people talking to a researcher and match them to the statements (a–e).

a used to live abroad ☐

b has seen TV programmes about emigrants ☐

c definitely isn't interested in living abroad ☐

d is planning to live abroad at some point ☐

e would like to live abroad but hasn't got any definite plans ☐

b Listen again and match the descriptions (a–e) with the people (1–5).

a is a university student ☐

b had problems with travel documents ☐

c is in a hurry ☐

d is worried about being identified ☐

e has family responsibilities ☐

c Now read the audioscript. Match words and phrases with the definitions (1–8).

1 thought about (noun) _____

2 make someone leave their home (verb) _____

3 interested in / fascinated by (-*ed* adjective + preposition) _____

4 depressing (adjective) _____

5 giving you a feeling you want to do something (-*ing* adjective) _____

6 this is my true feeling / opinion (phrase) _____

7 clearly (adverb) _____

8 chances (noun) _____

AUDIOSCRIPT

1

A: Excuse me. Can I ask you some questions about living abroad?

B: Sure.

A: Have you ever considered moving to a foreign country?

B: Not really. I'm quite happy with my life as it is! And I've got four kids, so it would be a bit difficult to uproot them from their schools and things, wouldn't it?

2

A: Hello. I'm doing some research on emigration. Can I talk to you for a minute?

B: OK. If it's quick. I'm a bit late for an appointment.

A: Thanks. Er, have you ever thought about moving abroad?

B: Yes. I'm quite intrigued by the idea of living somewhere else.

A: Any particular reason?

B: The weather, I suppose. It's so grim here in the winter, isn't it?

A: So you'd prefer somewhere hotter?

B: Probably. But I'm not really sure where ...

3

A: Excuse me. Can I ask you some questions about living in a foreign country?

B: Alright. You don't need my name or anything, do you?

A: No, nothing like that. I'd just like to ask you how you feel about the idea of moving abroad.

B: Oh, yes. I've seen those TV programmes about people moving to Australia. It always looks tempting.

A: Have you ever considered doing it yourself?

B: Myself? I've not really thought about it to be honest.

4

A: Excuse me. Hello. Could I just take a few minutes of your time? I'm doing some research on people emigrating, for my college course.

B: Really? I lived in Canada for a year when I was younger.

A: Oh, but obviously you came back ...

B: Well, I had this Canadian boyfriend. But it didn't really work out. And it was really difficult getting the right visas and things ...

5

A: Hi. Would you mind answering a few questions? It'll only take a minute or two.

B: Of course. No problem.

A: Have you ever considered emigrating?

B: I certainly have. I'd love to do it.

A: Why?

B: Well, the job opportunities, really. I'm in the middle of an engineering degree and when I finish I'm going to apply for jobs in the Middle East. There are loads of well-paid engineering posts over there ...

Grammar | modifying comparatives

2 Read the article and choose the correct words in *italics*.

The Ultimate Thrill

Everyone loves excitement and people say there is nothing (1) *just / quite* as exciting as a rollercoaster ride. For years, these rides were all fairly similar, with only small improvements – each new ride being (2) *slightly / nearly* more exciting than its predecessor.

But with the latest technological developments, new rollercoaster rides are (3) *far more / easily* exciting than ever before. Thrill-seekers looking for the ultimate rollercoaster ride are now torn between two monster rides on opposite sides of the world. By (4) *a lot / far* the biggest is Steel Dragon 2000 in Nagashima Spaland, a theme park 200 miles west of Tokyo. The ride is over one and a half miles long, lasts four minutes and includes a 68 degree drop. At times, riders reach speeds as fast (5) *than / as* 95 miles per hour. Costing $55 million, the ride was also a (6) *lot / much* more expensive to build than most other rides.

Steel Dragon 2000's arch rival is the Kingda Ka ride at Six Flags Great Adventure Park, near Philadelphia, in the US. It (7) *is / isn't* quite as long as its Japanese competitor, but what it lacks in size it makes up for in speed and height. With riders travelling at up to 128 miles per hour (206 kilometres per hour) it is (8) *by / just as* far the fastest rollercoaster ride on Earth. It is also (9) *slightly / easily* the tallest, with a height of 456 feet (139 metres). But at less than one minute, the ride is (10) *the / a* lot shorter than the four-minute experience of Steel Dragon 2000.

3 Find the mistakes in eight of these sentences and correct them.

1 Alvaro had by far the better results in the exam.

2 This exercise is bit more difficult than the last one.

3 The weather wasn't as hot as I'd expected.

4 I don't go to the gym as often that I used to.

5 The Mayback is easily the more expensive car BMW has ever made.

6 In the summer, Moscow can be the much warmer than most people expect.

7 This novel isn't nearly as interesting as his previous one.

8 If you want to pass the test, you'll have to answer the questions lot faster.

9 Antonio hasn't got quite as many friends on Facebook as I have.

10 I'm as tall just as my sister.

11 Could you speak little more slowly? I can't understand you.

12 Walter's new flat is far nicer than his previous one.

Vocabulary | verb phrases about moving/travelling

4 Match the sentence beginnings (1–8) with the sentence endings (a–h).

1 I've always dreamed about ☐

2 See you later. I'm ☐

3 Make sure you've got your passport and tickets before ☐

4 We hate the cold weather here so we're going ☐

5 Now that I'm 18 I think it's time ☐

6 She went to Greece and ☐

7 His girlfriend didn't even bother to go to the station ☐

8 We don't have enough bedrooms so we need ☐

a to emigrate.

b to move house.

c off to work.

d to see him off.

e roamed around the beaches.

f setting off.

g living abroad.

h to leave home.

Present Perfect Simple and Continuous

1 Complete the article using Past Simple, Present Perfect or Present Perfect Continuous forms of the verbs in brackets.

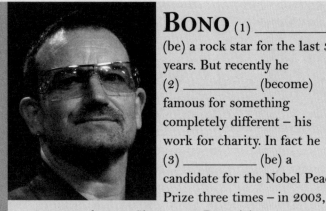

BONO (1) _____ (be) a rock star for the last 30 years. But recently he (2) _____ (become) famous for something completely different – his work for charity. In fact he (3) _____ (be) a candidate for the Nobel Peace Prize three times – in 2003, 2005 and 2006. Since 2003 Bono (4) _____ (lead) the fight against poverty in Africa, trying to get more people to understand that continent's terrible problems of famine and disease. For several years now he (5) _____ (appear) regularly on TV shows and at international events, attempting to get the world's media to pay attention to this issue. He (6) _____ (have) meetings with many world leaders and in 2005 he (7) _____ (help) organise the Live8 concerts in London and around the world. Bono lives in Dublin but spends much of his time travelling with his group, U2. Bono believes his position as an international celebrity (8) _____ (give) him a unique opportunity to influence young people. He (9) _____ (visit) Africa many times and these experiences (10) _____ (clearly influence) his political views. In 2003 Bono (11) _____ (meet) Nelson Mandela in Cape Town and in July 2005 he (12) _____ (speak) to world leaders at the G8 Conference in Scotland, helping to influence their decisions on reducing Africa's debt. Bono (13) _____ (appear) at the World Economic Forum meetings in Davos, Switzerland, several times. In 2008 he (14) _____ (make) a speech which linked the international debt crisis with growing concerns about global warming. Critics sometimes say that Bono (15) _____ (only do) this for the last ten years to compensate for his group's declining popularity. But with their latest CD high in the charts, this can hardly be the case.

Questions

2 There are eight incorrect questions in the dialogue. Find the mistakes and correct them.

¹**A:** Where went you for your holidays?
²**B:** We went to Florida.
³**A:** Who did go on holiday with you?
⁴**B:** My girlfriend.
⁵**A:** Can I ask what is her name?
⁶**B:** Of course. Her name's Lucy.
⁷**A:** Could you tell me what does she for a living?
⁸**B:** Yes. She's a hotel receptionist.
⁹**A:** Do you know how old she is?
¹⁰**B:** She's 21.
¹¹**A:** Can you tell me is she British?
¹²**B:** No. She's Australian.
¹³**A:** How long she has lived here?
¹⁴**B:** About six months.
¹⁵**A:** I'd like to know where did you meet.
¹⁶**B:** We met at a party.
¹⁷**A:** Why did you go to Florida?
¹⁸**B:** Well, we wanted to see Miami.
¹⁹**A:** Would you tell me how long did you stay in Florida?
²⁰**B:** We stayed there for three weeks.

Modifying comparatives

3 Choose the correct options (a, b or c). Sometimes more than one is possible.

1 I don't think Barcelona is _____ Malaga.
   a as sunny as   b quite sunnier than
   c nearly as sunny as

2 My new mobile is _____ my old one.
   a as better as   b a lot better than
   c far better than

3 They say Bill Gates is still _____ the richest man in America.
   a easily   b by far   c a lot

4 This model isn't _____ as expensive as the other ones with similar features.
   a quite   b just   c nearly

5 San Diego is usually _____ Los Angeles.
   a slightly hotter than   b a bit hot as
   c by far hotter than

6 Ella arrived _____ the others.
   a a bit later than   b much later than
   c just as late as

7 Did you drive _____ we did?
   a much further than   b a bit further than
   c just as further as

8 He takes life _____ than most people his age.
   a slightly more serious   b far more serious
   c a lot more seriously

Exploring

4 Find the mistake in each of these sentences and correct them.

1 I went as an independence traveller, not in a group.
2 Experiencing culture shocked can be one of the most difficult parts of living in a foreign country.
3 Do you make itchy feet or are you happy to stay in your home town?
4 My sister has always loved travelling – she was bitten by the journey bug as a teenager.
5 After a month away I began to feel housesick and was desperate to go back to my own country.
6 We never go on organised tours – we prefer to wonder around on our own.

Describing situations, feelings

5 Use the clues to complete the crossword.

1 I'm a bit ____ about Miriam. Is there something wrong with her?
2 She found the task ____ but she managed to achieve it in the end.
3 It's a ____ story, full of twists and turns that keep you interested.
4 I can't stand cabbage soup, I think it's ____ .
5 You shouldn't have told the children that scary story. They were ____ .
6 Picasso was ____ by African tribal art.
7 Babies are often ____ by brightly coloured objects.
8 That new horror film was absolutely ____ .
9 It's very ____ when people push in front of you at the supermarket check-out.
10 Some people feel ____ by marathons but I take them in my stride.

Weather

6 Complete the weather words with pairs of letters.

al   ar   ea   ee   ll   oo   ou   or   um   zz

1 cl____r
2 c____l
3 br____zy
4 p____r
5 h____id

6 dri____le
7 sc____ching
8 c____m
9 chi____y
10 w____m

Verb phrases about moving

7 Choose the correct words in *italics*.

1 I *moved/changed* house last year.
2 When I left for university my parents came to the station to see me *out/off*.
3 Their daughter lives *abroad/outside* so they don't see her very often.
4 Over a million Scots *migrated/emigrated* to the US in the 19th century.
5 The police found a small child roaming *round/around* in the streets.
6 When do you *go/set* off on your trip?
7 I was 16 when I left *home/house*.
8 I can't talk now. I'm *off/out* to meet my brother.

Expressions with *go*

8 Complete each sentence with one word.

1 Which car did you decide to go _____ ?
2 I'd love to _____ a go at ice-skating.
3 Do you think Johan will be able to _____ a go of the new business?
4 We'll pay – that goes _____ saying.
5 Trust me. I never go _____ on a promise.
6 I hope you like this CD. I went to great _____ to find it for you.
7 What's going _____ in the news?
8 Kieran's always on _____ go – he never seems to stand still!

How to...

9 Complete each sentence with one word.

1 The sooner you see the doctor, the _____ you'll feel better.
2 We went skating on the frozen pond, _____ was incredibly exciting!
3 The _____ I practised, the better I became.
4 I took plenty of warm clothes, _____ three thick pullovers!
5 The more you work, the _____ time you have to spend with your family.

Listening

1 a 🔵 10 Cover the audioscript. Listen to an extract from a radio programme about epic films. Complete the table with a number or a word.

Hollywood's greatest historical epics

Gladiator, released in 2000, earned more than (1) $_____ million at the box office.

Ben Hur, (2) _____ , was (3) _____ by William Wyler.

Spartacus was released in (4) _____ .

El Cid, (5) _____ , tells the story of (6) _____ hero Rodrigo Diaz.

Lawrence of Arabia, 1962, featured a young Irish (7) _____ , Peter O'Toole.

Cleopatra was a big hit in (8) _____ (9) _____ Elizabeth Taylor.

Troy was released in (10) _____ .

---

b Listen again. Which film(s) is the speaker talking about?

1 perhaps the greatest epic of them all
   _____

2 Ridley Scott's inspiration for *Gladiator*
   _____

3 the most expensive film ever made at the time
   _____

4 disappointing box office _____

5 almost bankrupted its makers _____

6 went on to win five Oscars _____

c Now read the audioscript. Match words and phrases with the definitions (1–8).

1 being ignored / sleeping _____

2 type _____

3 period of greatness _____

4 buildings created for a film _____

5 excellent _____

6 together with _____

7 huge amount of money _____

8 actors in a film who don't speak _____

AUDIOSCRIPT

(a) One of the most remarkable developments in the recent history of film-making was the revival of the historical epic at the start of the 21st century. After lying dormant for almost 40 years, this spectacular and lavish genre of film-making made an unexpected reappearance with Ridley Scott's *Gladiator* in 2000. After the film (1) _____ five Oscars and its makers (2) _____ over $458 million at the box office, Hollywood was forced to re-examine this area of film-making.

(b) So, what exactly is a historical epic? To explain that, we have to go back to the late 1950s and the film that marked the start of the brief golden age of the epic, *Ben Hur*. This film had all the classic ingredients of the historical epic. **(c)** It was long, it was set in a long distant period of history, it featured lots of battles, and it had big stars and even bigger sets. The film was released in 1959 but its director, William Wyler, (3) _____ on it for more than six years and (4) _____ $15 million – making it the most expensive film ever made at the time. But it went on to gain 11 Oscars and huge profits for MGM.

(d) There followed a series of superb epic films. In 1960 there was legendary director Stanley Kubrick's powerful *Spartacus*, starring Kirk Douglas and Laurence Olivier – the film that was in fact Ridley Scott's inspiration for *Gladiator*. The next year, Charlton Heston, the star of *Ben Hur*, appeared alongside Sophia Loren in *El Cid*, the moving story of Spanish hero Rodrigo Diaz's attempts to drive the Moors out of Spain. 1962 saw the release of perhaps the greatest epic of them all, **(e)** and my personal favourite, David Lean's *Lawrence of Arabia*, featuring a young Irish actor who (5) _____ on screen before – Peter O'Toole.

The end of this short golden age came in 1963 with the release of *Cleopatra*. Directed by Joseph L. Mankiewicz and starring Elizabeth Taylor, the film had cost a fortune to make and was never able to make a profit at the box office, causing financial difficulties for its makers. By the early 1960s, television (6) _____ to eclipse films, cinema attendances were falling and the amounts of money film-makers were earning were simply too small to cover the enormous production costs of historical epics.

This changed with the advent of computer-generated imaging, or CGI as it is known. For years, directors (7) _____ to use computers to generate film images, but the computers available (8) _____ powerful enough. This all changed in the late 1990s. **(f)** Suddenly it was possible to have as many soldiers and horses, Roman arenas and Trojan city walls as you wanted, without having to pay extras or build huge sets. But with the disappointing box office for Wolfgang Petersen's *Troy* of 2004 and Oliver Stone's *Alexander* also of 2004, this second golden age of the historical epic proved to be fairly short-lived.

How to... | engage your listener

2 The speaker uses a range of tenses and time expressions. Match the ways to make what you're saying sound interesting (1–4) with the underlined parts of the audioscript (a–f).

1 use rhetorical questions ☐
2 include your personal response ☐
3 introduce what you're going to say ☐ , ☐
4 include details ☐ , ☐

Grammar | Past Perfect Simple and Continuous

3 Look at the audioscript again. Complete the gaps (1–8) with Past Perfect Simple or Continuous form of verbs from the box. Then listen again and check your answers.

> begin   earn   spend   never appear   not be   try
> win   work

4 Use the information in the pictures to complete the sentences (1–4). Use the Past Perfect Simple or Continuous.

1 Alex was late for work because _____ .

2 Dave was covered in oil because _____ .

3 Karl _____ all night, so he was exhausted when he got to school in the morning.

4 Susy didn't want to rent the DVD of *Avatar* because _____ .

5 Complete the sentences (1–8) using Past Perfect Simple or Continuous forms of the verbs from the box. Use the continuous whenever possible.

> not do   not drive   leave   lie   not see
> talk   wait   work

1 By lunchtime, Lauren was exhausted because she _____ hard all morning.
2 I _____ a 3D movie before so I was very excited about going to see *Avatar*.
3 When she came into the house, Carla's skin was very red – she _____ in the sun all day.
4 I got a really low mark in the exam because I _____ enough revision.
5 Steve had to pay for the meal in cash because he _____ his credit card at home.
6 By the time we got to the front of the queue, we _____ for more than two hours.
7 I knew Sally was going to marry Roberto because she _____ about him for months and months!
8 When I arrived in Australia I found the driving difficult – I _____ on the left hand side of the road before.

Vocabulary | time expressions

6 Complete the sentences (1–8) using words or phrases from the box. One is not needed.

> after that   at that time   during   until
> for the previous   from that point on
> since then   throughout   while

1 _____ century, the two countries had been at war.
2 I stopped smoking three years ago and I haven't had a single cigarette _____ .
3 I was surprised to get a phone call _____ breakfast.
4 Margaret Thatcher was Prime Minister of the UK _____ the 1980s.
5 _____ , in the late 1950s, there were almost no supermarkets in England.
6 We missed our connecting flight and _____ things just got worse.
7 Giovanni used to look after the children _____ Clara was at work.
8 The mechanic arrived and repaired our car. _____ , we were able to continue on our journey.

Reading

1 **a** Read the article and answer the questions.

1 What are convenience stores?

_____

2 What is sometimes surprising about these places?

_____

3 Who usually works in these stores in London?

_____

4 How do these stores find employees?

_____

5 How are family members paid for their work?

_____

b Replace the underlined words and phrases in the sentences (1–8) with words and phrases from the article.

1 Harrods is a <u>famous</u> department store in London. _____

2 They've just bought a <u>large</u> house. _____

3 People who live in the country are sometimes more relaxed than <u>people who live in a city</u>. _____

4 We <u>hardly ever</u> take holidays. _____

5 The government is considering changing the law on <u>people moving to this country from another one</u>. _____

6 My parents <u>own and manage</u> a dry cleaning business. _____

7 I have never understood the <u>financial basis</u> of international trade. _____

8 The <u>origin</u> of the River Nile is in Uganda. _____

Asian Shopping

Visitors to London, New York and Los Angeles often remark on how easy it is to buy (1) _____ things at any time of the day. It isn't the well-known department stores, large supermarkets or huge shopping malls that they are talking about but those tiny shops (2) _____ Americans call 'convenience stores' and the British call 'corner shops'. They may not always be situated on corners, but they are certainly convenient for tourists and for those city-dwellers who work long hours and don't have time to shop during the day. As people in large cities work longer and longer hours the availability of late-night shopping has become a necessity rather than a luxury.

(3) _____ other thing that sometimes causes surprise is that these shops are rarely owned or staffed by local people. The English-sounding names of 'Super Saver', 'Bargain Supplies' or 'Mini-market'

give no clue to the origin of the people working inside the store. In fact, they often seem to be staffed by (4) _____ people from various parts of Asia. Their nationalities often reflect the history of immigration to the country concerned, and they frequently come from nations with a reputation for successful trade and shop-keeping. In New York and Los Angeles it is often Koreans and Chinese who run these stores and in London it is people from the Indian sub-continent.

But what are the economics of such places? How can tiny shops make any profit when employees have to be paid to work (5) _____ such long hours? (6) _____ answer lies partly in the Asian culture of hard work, but is mainly due to the tradition of the extended family. This is very different from the typical Western family in which the individual members have separate lives and careers. When (7) _____ Asian family owns a shop everyone gets involved – brothers, sisters, uncles, aunts, cousins, grandparents and children – everybody is expected to work behind the counter. Thus there is (8) _____ guaranteed source of staff available to work from early morning until late at (9) _____ night. And rather than being paid salaries, the members of the family simply share in (10) _____ profits at the end of the year. It is a recipe that has brought wealth to many immigrant families and made life a lot easier for those of us who run out of milk at 11 o'clock on a Sunday evening!

Grammar | articles

2 Complete the gaps in the article (1–10) in exercise 1a with *a, an, the* or the zero article (–).

3 Ten of the sentences (1–15) contain mistakes. Find the mistakes and correct them.

1 Would you prefer milk or cream in your coffee?

2 Janine and Mike have got beautiful garden.

3 She'd been living in the Los Angeles since the 1980s.

4 Heathrow is the busiest airport in the UK.

5 When I was young I wanted to be astronaut.

6 Let's have another look at a first one they showed us.

7 I think mobile phone is the greatest invention ever.

8 Teresa's first husband was an engineer.

9 Rudolf's planning to study the philosophy at university.

10 Have you got the double room with a sea view?

11 The Azores are in the middle of Atlantic Ocean.

12 Geography was my favourite subject at school.

13 I love looking at a moon at night.

14 This is most exciting book I've read for a long time.

15 St Moritz is one of the most expensive ski resorts in the Alps.

Pronunciation | connected speech: elision

4 **a** 🔊 11 Listen to five sentences and write down what you hear.

1 _____
_____

2 _____
_____

3 _____
_____

4 _____
_____

5 _____
_____

b Check your answers on page 86. Did you miss any articles?

Vocabulary | materials

5 Use the clues to complete the crossword.

Across

2 antique vases are made from it

5 good material for summer clothes

7 slightly elastic

9 has a bright surface

10 car tyres

11 the opposite of smooth

13 a strong metal

14 perfect for a wedding dress

Down

1 comes from trees

3 shoes and belts

4 opposite of hard

6 has an even surface

7 when something gets wet

8 like something animals have to keep them warm

12 a wedding ring

How to... | reach an agreement

6 Choose the correct words in *italics*.

A: Which do you think is the most important invention, planes or cars?

B: Well, if you (1) *put/take* into account the number of people who use them, I suppose cars are more important.

A: That's a good (2) *point/argue*. But you can't really (3) *discuss/say* that cars have changed the world, can you? They just do the same thing that horses used to do.

B: Yeah, (4) *you're/you've* right. They can only take us over land. In planes you can fly all over the world.

A: Right, so we agree (5) *for/on* planes.

Reading

1 **a** Read the factfile about five leading multinational companies and tick (✓) the correct column.

	Nestlé	Coca-Cola	Zara	Shell	Gap
1 the youngest company					
2 the oldest company					
3 has the most shops					
4 has the highest value of sales					
5 based in Switzerland					
6 founded in London					
7 employs the most people					
8 employs the fewest people					
9 famous for its advertisements					
10 owns businesses in 200 countries					

b Match words in the factfile with the definitions (1–8).

1 drinks _____

2 company that makes products _____

3 doesn't include alcohol _____

4 started a company _____

5 company that takes products to different locations _____

6 famous names belonging to a company _____

7 throughout the world _____

8 eaten or drunk _____

Multinational Factfile

Zara is one of Europe's best known brands of clothes stores. It is part of the Inditex group, based in La Coruña, Spain. The first Zara shop opened in La Coruña in 1975. The group now owns 2,692 stores in 81 countries. Its sales are 6.2 billion euros (around nine billion dollars) and it employs 92,000 people.

Nestlé was founded by Henri Nestlé in 1866. Its headquarters are in Vevey, Switzerland. Nestlé is currently the world's largest manufacturer of food and beverages, with international sales of 88 billion Swiss Francs ($89.5 billion). Nestle employs 281,000 people all over the world.

Shell is a multinational company famous for its petrol stations and oil production facilities. Founded by Marcus Samuel in London in 1833, the company merged with the Royal Dutch group in 1907. Shell's international headquarters is now in the Hague, Holland. Shell operates in 90 countries and employs around 101,000 people. Shell generates sales in the region of $278 billion from its worldwide operations.

Coca-Cola is based in Atlanta, Georgia, US. Founded in 1886, it is now the world's largest manufacturer and distributor of non-alcoholic beverages. Through the 400 businesses it owns in 200 different countries, it employs around one million people. It is estimated that 1.3 billion Coca-Cola drinks are consumed every day. Its sales are worth almost 29 billion dollars per year.

Famous for its clothes stores and imaginative advertising campaigns, Gap is one of the world's most recognisable clothing brands. The first Gap store opened in San Francisco, California, in 1969, and the company is still based in this city. There are now over 3,200 Gap stores, employing 134,000 people. The company achieves sales of around $15 billion annually.

Pronunciation | speech units

2 **a** Look at the paragraph in the factfile about Shell. Prepare to read it aloud by writing // in the places where you would pause.

b 🔘 12 Listen and check.

Grammar | adjectives and adverbs

3 Write the word in brackets in the correct position.

The clients will expect to get a discount. (certainly)

The clients will certainly expect to get a discount.

1 When I have a headache all I want to do is lie down. (bad)

_____

_____

2 He didn't work so he was bound to fail the exam. (hard)

_____

_____

3 You're very early; did you drive? (fast)

_____

_____

4 Anna is always dressed in designer outfits. (expensively)

_____

_____

5 Some of these new computer games are challenging. (incredibly)

_____

_____

6 It snowed throughout our holiday. (heavily)

_____

_____

7 He interrupted me in the middle of my speech. (rudely)

_____

_____

8 Do you know them? (well)

_____

_____

9 I'm going to take the First Certificate Exam this year. (definitely)

_____

_____

10 The weather can be hot in September. (surprisingly)

_____

_____

4 Match the underlined phrases with phrases from the box. Three of the phrases are not needed.

> completely ruined   recently   hard   hardly
> high   late   near   nearly   probably
> reasonably priced   unbelievably   unlikely
> well

1 This new computer is not expensive at all. _____
2 Our holiday was totally spoilt by the awful weather. _____
3 She hasn't been coming to lessons in the last few weeks. _____
4 The class found the exercise difficult. _____
5 My uncle speaks Polish fluently. _____
6 We'll almost certainly move to the country next year. _____
7 My son is almost six years old now. _____
8 Jimmy getting a promotion seems rather hard to believe. _____
9 Sheila handed in her essay after it was due. _____
10 The plane flew at a great height over the city. _____

Vocabulary | verb phrases with *take*

5 Choose the correct option to complete the sentences.

1 Nearly all the students ____ the survey.
   a took part of   b took in   c took part in
2 You should never take good health ____ .
   a for grant   b as granted   c for granted
3 A Korean company has ____ that old factory.
   a taken over   b taken up   c taken out
4 I tried it for a month but I didn't really ____ that new diet.
   a take to   b take at   c take in
5 Seeing the sun set over the mountains really took my breath ____ .
   a over   b out   c away
6 He wasn't paying much attention so he didn't take ____ .
   a it in all   b it all in   c it all through
7 It didn't worry me at all, I took ____ .
   a it in the stride   b all in my stride
   c it all in my stride
8 The use of electric cars has never really ____ in the US.
   a taken off   b taken part in
   c taken out

Past Perfect Simple and Continuous

1 Match the sentence starters (1–8) with the sentence endings (a or b).

1 Millie was dirty and covered in dust – she ☐
2 Sally's friends were able to stay in the loft – she ☐
  a had been cleaning the loft all morning.
  b had cleaned it before they arrived.
3 By the time I got down to the swimming pool the other guests ☐
4 Most of the people around the swimming pool were quite tanned – they ☐
  a had been sunbathing all day.
  b had taken all the sun beds.
5 When he got home Jack collapsed onto the sofa, exhausted – he ☐
6 Sergio retired at the age of 65 – he ☐
  a had worked at the factory for 15 years.
  b had been working at the factory all day.
7 Alex was sweaty and out of breath – he ☐
8 Boris felt proud of himself because, despite being in his 60s, he ☐
  a had been running a marathon.
  b had run in three marathons.

Articles

2 Choose the correct words in *italics*.

Isambard Kingdom Brunel was (1) *most/the most/ a most* famous British engineer of the 19th century.

Born in 1806 in (2) *a Portsmouth/the Portsmouth/ Portsmouth*, his first major work was the construction of a railway between London and Bristol in the west of England. The construction of (3) *a railway/the railway/ railway* involved building (4) *a tunnel/tunnel/the tunnel* near the town of Box in Somerset. It was three kilometres long, (5) *longest/a longest/the longest* tunnel ever constructed at the time.

After his success with railways, Brunel turned his attention to (6) *the ships/ships*. He wanted to connect his railway line in Bristol with New York in (7) *United States/ a United States/the United States*. In 1838 he built the 'Great Western', the first large steam-powered ship, which crossed (8) *the Atlantic/Atlantic/an Atlantic* in only 15 days.

Brunel's next project was to build (9) *the ship/a ship/ship* made of iron. He achieved this in 1843 with the 'Great Britain'. It was also the first to be driven by (10) *a propeller/the propeller*.

(11) *The ambition/An ambition/Ambition* and (12) *the stubbornness/a stubbornness/stubbornness* were the greatest features of Brunel's character; he always strove to design the biggest and best.

Adjectives and adverbs

3 Find the mistakes in eight of these sentences and correct them.

1 Heinrich often arrives lately for work.
2 We had to drive slowly because of the heavy rain.
3 I find people around here are general quite friendly.
4 She's much better; she's feeling finely today.
5 My sister can type amazingly quick.
6 Despite studying hardly, Maria failed the test.
7 Have you seen any good films recently?
8 I thought that book was more interestingly than the others.
9 Have you ever noticed how highly frogs can jump?
10 This is definite the best restaurant we've been to for ages.

4 Put the words in the correct order to make sentences.

1 The / in /professor / friendly / a / treats / all / his / way / students/ .
  _____
2 Isabel / is / oldest / the /student / definitely / our / in / class/ .
  _____
3 I / this /washed / morning / sheets / the / .
  _____
4 My / forgets / sometimes / brother / his / number / PIN /.
  _____
5 Daniela / in / the / left /of / the / room / corner / her / suitcase / .
  _____
6 The / forgot / children / stupidly / to / their / costumes / swimming / bring /.
  _____
7 He / driving, / but / quite /he / wasn't / dangerously /was / going / fast / .
  _____
8 She / personality / warm / has / a / and / caring / .
  _____

Age and time expressions

5 Use the clues to complete the crossword.

Across

4 What is the ___ dress of your country?

5 I got a job in March but for the ___ two months I was unemployed.

6 The Pyramids are the greatest monuments of ___ Egypt.

8 There was rationing ___ the Second World War.

9 My grandmother is in a home for ___ people.

Down

1 Some of my aunt's clothes are very old-___.

2 Up until that ___ I had been an engineer.

3 ___ clothes aren't always expensive.

6 That old hotel is full of beautiful ___ furniture.

7 What will life be like in the 22nd ___?

Materials and describing objects

6 **a** Match the objects (1–7) with the materials (a–g).

1	a wedding ring	a	silk
2	a pair of swimming trunks	b	leather
3	bed sheets	c	rubber
4	a pair of jeans	d	denim
5	a wedding dress	e	gold
6	car tyres	f	cotton
7	expensive shoes	g	lycra

b Match the objects (1–5) with the descriptions (a–e).

1	a mirror	a	stretchy
2	ice on a road	b	soft
3	a cushion	c	shiny
4	an elastic band	d	rough
5	a mountain path	e	slippery

Verb phrases with *take*

7 Choose the correct words in *italics*.

1 Watching the sunset in Hawaii took my breath *out/away*.

2 It's very hard to take *in/out* all this information.

3 Marco's relaxed about what happened; he took it all in his *steps/stride*.

4 Mr Lester is going to take *under/over* the Glasgow branch.

5 Young people often take modern technology completely *for/of* granted.

6 I'm taking part *in/at* a demonstration against the war.

7 Dan took *at/to* his fiancée's parents as soon as he met them.

8 Playing cricket has never really taken *out/off* in Europe.

Making nouns

8 Replace the underlined phrases with nouns.

Professor Grant is a person who invents things.
an inventor

1 Emma loves being a mother. _____

2 Having friends is the most important thing for Pepe. _____

3 David is a person who plays the piano professionally. _____

4 We need to increase the amount we produce. _____

5 Being happy is more important than wealth. _____

6 I'm not very pleased with the things you arranged. _____

How to…

9 Match the phrases (1–6) with the uses (a–f).

1 'You can't really say that.' ☐

2 'Yes, that's a good point.' ☐

3 'I think that people who …' ☐

4 'Now, what did he do?' ☐

5 'Right, so we agree on the computer.' ☐

6 'He was born in the Kalahari.' ☐

a Include details

b Use rhetorical questions

c Argue against someone's point

d Include your personal response

e Concede a point

f State an agreed point

4 Work

Listening

1 **a** 🔘 13 Cover the audioscript. Listen to four people talking about their jobs. Match the speakers (1–4) with the jobs from the box. Four of the jobs are not needed.

> ballet dancer   engineer   secretary   actor
> architect   photographer   journalist
> hotel receptionist

1 _____

2 _____

3 _____

4 _____

b Listen again and complete the expressions (1–8). Then match the expressions with the definitions (a–h).

Speaker 1

1 I'm a natural _____ , I suppose. ☐

2 There's a sort of _____ that you get from an audience. ☐

Speaker 2

3 I never meant to get into this _____ . ☐

4 ... it all sort of _____ from there. ☐

5 But I'm _____ so basically ... ☐

Speaker 3

6 ... some of the guests are _____ ! ☐

Speaker 4

7 I had _____ space ships and futuristic cities for some reason. ☐

8 ... designing is something that's _____ . ☐

a   difficult to manage/deal with

b   person who likes to be the centre of attention

c   an obsession with

d   developed/grew rapidly

e   career or profession

f   part of your basic personality

g   feeling of excitement

h   self-employed

c Complete the audioscript using appropriate forms of the verbs from the box below. Then listen and check.

> appear   take   live

AUDIOSCRIPT

1

I'm a natural show off, I suppose. Even as a kid I loved performing in front of other people. Whenever the family got together, my parents used to get me to stand on the table, singing songs and doing little scenes. There's a sort of buzz that you get from an audience that nothing else quite matches up to. In fact, I (1) _____ on stage again next month, which should make a nice change from all the TV work.

2

It all happened by accident, really. I mean – I never meant to get into this line of work. In fact, when I was young I wanted to be a ballerina! But when I was at university a friend persuaded me to take some pictures for the college magazine, and it all sort of snowballed from there. The fashion shoots are the ones I enjoy most. But I'm freelance so basically I (2) _____ any assignment that's on offer. Even weddings!

3

The really great thing about my job is the number and variety of people you meet. Not that they are all nice – some of the guests are a real handful! But however bad they are, you always know that they'll be leaving in a few days, so that makes it bearable. And of course, I often get the chance to use my languages.

4

Even when I was quite small I loved drawing. I had a thing for space ships and futuristic cities for some reason! Well, of course, I don't really do any actual drawing now – the computers do it all for us! But designing is something that's in the blood, and the great thing about my job is that it's not just theoretical, because you know real people (3) _____ and work in the things you've designed ...

Vocabulary | work

2 Complete the sentences using the correct form of phrases from the box. Two are not needed.

> work from home   commute   paid employment
> do voluntary work   workaholic   workplace
> work-rhythm   work-centred culture
> nine-to-five working day   flexible working day

1 I can vary my work hours to suit my other commitments.
  I have a _____

2 My mother helps at the local old people's home, although she doesn't get paid.
  My mother _____

3 Tomas hates the long journey from home to work every morning.
  Tomas doesn't like _____

4 I've just converted the guest bedroom into my new office.
  Now I can _____

5 My father seemed to work all the time, it was an obsession for him.
  My father was _____

6 Pedro's parents are very wealthy so he doesn't need to work for a living.
  Pedro doesn't need _____

7 In some countries, work seems to be the most important thing in life.
  Some countries seem to have _____

8 The government has made it illegal to smoke in offices, factories and shops.
  It is now illegal to smoke _____

Grammar | futures (1)

3 Choose the best explanation (a or b).

1 Alison's bound to get that job in New York. ☐
  a I expect this to happen.
  b I don't know whether this will happen or not.

2 Mr Askew's on the verge of resigning. ☐
  a He's probably going to leave his job next year.
  b He's probably going to leave soon.

3 Take some sun cream – it'll be hot there next month. ☐
  a I've just seen the weather forecast.
  b I know it's always hot there at this time of year.

4 Look. Baxter's going to win the race. ☐
  a Baxter is the fastest runner.
  b I can see that Baxter is in front of the other runners.

5 Amanda's about to take her driving test. ☐
  a Amanda's driving test is tomorrow.
  b Amanda's driving test is next month.

6 I think I'll have a tuna salad. ☐
  a I've just decided to get a salad.
  b I'm talking about my plans for tomorrow's lunch.

7 We're taking the kids to Bodrum in August. ☐
  a We hope to get the tickets next week.
  b We booked our flights yesterday.

8 Watch out! You're going to slip. ☐
  a I can see a patch of oil on the ground.
  b I know you've been unsteady on your feet since your accident.

How to... | talk about future plans

4 Complete the sentences using the words in brackets.

1 Mia's well qualified so she's bound to leave
  _____
  (the / next / in / so / month / or)

2 Look at those dark clouds – there's going to be a storm _____
  (about / in / an / hour's / time)

3 Claire's really upset –
  _____ I think she's on the verge of leaving her husband.
  (not / I'm / but / sure / yet)

4 _____ but I haven't made a definite decision yet.
  (leaving / thinking / I'm / about)

5 My mother will be 40 years old
  _____
  (coming / this / October)

6 We're not sure about our next holiday but _____ to Disney Land.
  (take / is / one / possibility / the kids / to)

7 Turn on the TV – _____ the election results.
  (about / announce / are / they / to)

8 The company hasn't made any decision on redundancies. _____ situation.
  (all / economic / It / on / depends / the)

Reading

1 **a** Read the article and answer the questions.

1 What does the word *guilt* in the title refer to?

_____

2 Why is the weight of the sculpture significant?

_____

3 What happens to 90% of Europe's electronic waste?

_____

b Read the article again and add two more examples to each part of the list.

- **Adjectives:** *terrifying,* _____ , _____
- **Adverbs:** *ingeniously,* _____ , _____
- **Body:** *head,* _____ , _____
- **Electronics:** *computers,* _____ , _____
- **Appliances:** *cookers,* _____ , _____

c Match words or phrases in the article with the meanings (1–10).

1 thrown away (adj, para 1) _____

2 when someone paid an artist to make a particular work (verb, para 1) _____

3 wasteful (adj, para 1) _____

4 advanced (compound adj, para 1) _____

5 wires connecting electrical appliances (noun, para 2) _____

6 devices held in your hand which control computers (noun, para 2) _____

7 promote/persuade (verb, para 3) _____

8 now (adv, para 3) _____

9 places where rubbish is stored and covered with earth (compound noun, para 3) _____

10 burned (verb, para 3) _____

Sculpture of Guilt

(1) This is 'Weee Man', a terrifying metal and plastic sculpture created by Paul Bonomini from discarded computers, electronic components and domestic products. Commissioned by the Royal Society of Arts (RSA), the sculpture stands 24 feet (7 metres) high beside the river Thames in London and serves as a shocking reminder of the huge amount of waste produced by today's extravagant high-tech society.

(2) The main body of the figure includes three washing machines, five fridges, seven vacuum cleaners, 35 mobile phones and 12 kettles, plus assorted microwaves, televisions, radiators and sections of ducting and cabling. The artist has ingeniously created the head from a combination of surprising elements. The teeth are in fact computer mice, the eyes are washing machine doors and the ears are satellite dishes.

(3) The name of the sculpture, 'Weee', comes from the phrase Waste Electrical and Electronic Equipment, and its weight, 3.3 tonnes, is the same as the weight of electrical equipment thrown away by an average person in a lifetime. The RSA hopes that the sculpture will encourage recycling by dramatically reminding us of the sheer quantity of products we throw away unnecessarily. Citizens of the European Union currently produce 6.5 million tonnes of electronic waste a year, most of which ends up in landfill sites or is incinerated. A mere 10% is recycled.

Grammar | Future Perfect and Future Continuous

2 Write answers to the questions using the prompts. Use appropriate forms of the Future Perfect or Future Continuous.

A: Will you have finished work by 5.30?

B: No, I / not finish / until six

No, I won't have finished until six.

1 **A:** Will you be going on holiday next July?

   B: No, I / go / in August instead

   _____

2 **A:** Do you think Henry will have finished the project by the time I get back?

   B: Yes, he / should / finish / it by then

   _____

3 **A** Will Mr Simpson be able to see me between four and five?

   B: No, I'm afraid he / see / another client then

   _____

4 **A:** Can we start work on the building site next January?

   B: Yes, we / should / receive / planning permission / by then

   _____

5 **A:** Will the children be joining you for the summer?

   B: Yes, they / stay / with us from July to September

   _____

6 **A:** Can we meet in the office tomorrow?

   B: No, I / work / at home all day tomorrow

   _____

7 **A:** How are you getting on with the decorating?

   B: Pretty well. By the end of next month we should / finish / most of it

   _____

8 **A:** Will Gabriella's report be ready for the meeting this afternoon?

   B: Yes, she / do / it by lunchtime at the latest

   _____

3 Complete the dialogues using the Future Perfect or Future Continuous forms of the verbs in brackets.

1 **A:** Can I watch the cartoons now, Mum?

   B: No. You can wait until after dinner.

   A: But they _____ by then! (finish)

2 **A:** Do you think we'll get there in time?

   B: No, I don't. By the time we get there, the train _____ . (leave)

3 **A:** Next week's going to be really busy.

   B: Not for me! This time next week I _____ on a beach in Sardinia. (lie)

4 **A:** Is Deirdre coming to the party on her own?

   B: No. She _____ her boyfriend. (bring)

5 **A:** I don't want to spend hours waiting for her at the airport.

   B: Don't worry. I'm sure Jan _____ by the time we get there. (arrive)

Vocabulary | verb phrases about time

4 Find the mistakes in five of these sentences and correct them.

1 There's no rush to finish the job – you can make your time.

2 I wanted to finish the project but I ran out from time.

3 Let's drive there on the motorway – it'll save time.

4 We had some time to murder before our flight so we had a coffee and a sandwich.

5 However busy they are, people really need to make time for some relaxation.

6 If I have time for sparing, I like to surf the Internet.

7 Now that the children are at school, Mariza has gone back to working complete-time at the local bakery.

8 My grandmother passes the time by doing crossword puzzles.

How to... | make your point in a confident way

5 Choose the correct words in *italics*.

1 I understand your point of view, I *very/really* do.

2 Without *doubt/doubting*, I'd say that work is the most important part of my life.

3 My job isn't as satisfying as my family life, *of/for* sure.

4 Believe *it/me*, I often struggle to find time for my husband and kids.

5 The *fact is/facts are* I have a very demanding job and I'm under a lot of pressure.

Pronunciation | stress: sounding sure

6 a Look at the sentences. Underline the words you think are stressed.

1 I understand your point of view, I really do.

2 My job isn't as satisfying as my family life, for sure.

3 The fact is I have a very demanding job and I'm under a lot of pressure.

b 🔵 14 Listen and check your answers. Then repeat the sentences.

Reading

1 **a** Read the website and match the headings (a–f) with the paragraphs (1–6).

a Health-care workers ☐ d What is a uniform? ☐

b Security and the armed forces ☐ e Schools ☐

c Sports ☐ f Corporate clothing ☐

1 A uniform is a set of standard clothing worn by members of an organisation while participating in that organisation's activity. Modern uniforms are worn by armed forces and paramilitary organisations such as the police, emergency services, security guards, in some workplaces and schools and by inmates in prisons. In some countries, other officials such as customs and immigration officers, traffic wardens and judges also wear uniforms when on duty. For certain groups which have particular powers over members of the public, such as the police, it is illegal for non-members to wear the uniform.

2 As part of their attempt to project a commercial 'brand', large companies often require their workers to wear a uniform. This includes the employees of banks, supermarkets, health clubs, hotels and restaurant chains. Uniforms are particularly common for workers who need to exercise some form of authority over the public, such as security guards and flight attendants.

3 Workers in institutions such as hospitals often wear uniforms. The 'white coat' has become an international symbol for doctors. Nursing staff often have special uniforms which indicate their particular role. Patients in hospital are also frequently made to wear particular clothes. As well as indicating the wearer's role, hospital uniforms also fulfill an important function in maintaining hygienic standards.

4 Most, if not all, professional sports teams wear uniforms, made in the team's distinctive colours, often in different variations for 'home' and 'away' games. In Britain, the terms *kit* or *strip* (as in *rugby kit*) are more common than *uniform*. Supporters of teams can often buy themselves versions of sports kit to wear and the sale of these items is an important source of income for many teams.

5 Military personnel usually wear complex uniforms which indicate the precise role and rank of the wearer. In fact, the use of uniforms probably originates with the need for soldiers to identify their officers during battles. Military uniforms are divided into two types: *battledress*, which is worn everyday; and *dress uniform*, which is worn for official ceremonies. Dress uniform can be very elaborate and varies greatly from country to country.

6 Across the world, uniforms are worn in many educational institutions. Uniforms vary from a standard issue T-shirt to rigorous requirements for many items of formal wear at private and some state schools. Countries with mandatory school uniforms include Japan, India, Australia and many schools in Britain and China. Teachers at some schools and universities can also wear a uniform for special occasions, often a black 'gown' which is worn on top of ordinary clothes.

b Read the website again and match the sentences (1–8) with features from the box.

> military   educational   police   sport
> health   corporate

1 Sales of uniforms to the public are important for financial reasons. _____

2 Uniforms are often worn for reasons of hygiene. _____

3 It is against the law for non-members to wear this uniform. _____

4 The uniform is often a standard T-shirt. _____

5 The uniform shows the exact rank of the wearer. _____

6 The uniform helps to present a company's brand. _____

7 One example has become an international symbol. _____

8 There are two different types of uniform. _____ , _____

Grammar | verb patterns: *-ing* forms and infinitives

2 Complete the sentences using an appropriate form of the verb in brackets.

1 Our parents always encouraged us _____ hard at school. (work)

2 I avoid _____ taxis because they are so expensive. (take)

3 Did you remember _____ them a text message with our arrival time? (send)

4 My doctor advised me _____ the amount of salt in my diet. (cut down)

5 Why don't you try _____ the 'restart' button – that usually works. (press)

6 I'm going to carry on _____ for jobs until I eventually get one! (apply)

7 We regret _____ you that all tickets for the concert have been sold out. (inform)

8 Mr Adamson allowed his students _____ calculators in the maths exam. (use)

9 Will you stop _____ when you get to 65? (work)

10 I'm glad the shop assistant suggested _____ an extra pair of shoes. (buy)

3 Put the words in order to make sentences.

1 allowed / to / early. / Our / teacher / us / leave
_____

2 learn / me / My / parents / a / musical / instrument. / encouraged / to
_____

3 upgrade / the / check-in clerk / to / him / to / persuaded / business class. / Danny
_____

4 advised / some / weight. / lose / to / The / doctor / Sara
_____

5 someone / saw / the / over / wall. / I / climbing
_____

6 the / boss. / arguing / with / his / Viktor / colleague / heard
_____

4 Match the sentence beginnings (1–14) with the sentence endings (a–b).

1 I stopped watching TV ☐
2 I stopped to watch TV ☐
   a and answered the phone.
   b because there was a fascinating documentary on.
3 I regret to say ☐
4 I regret saying ☐
   a you were lazy, it was very rude of me.
   b that you have not been selected for the team.
5 I remember locking the door before ☐
6 Remember to lock the door before ☐
   a you go home.
   b I left.
7 Hilary tried closing the door but ☐
8 Hilary tried to close the door but ☐
   a there was still a cold draught in the room.
   b it was jammed and she couldn't do it.
9 I saw my neighbour hanging out her washing ☐
10 I saw my neighbour hang out her washing ☐
   a and go back into the house.
   b while I was gardening.
11 We heard the orchestra playing Beethoven's Ninth Symphony ☐
12 We heard the orchestra play Beethoven's ninth symphony ☐
   a as we walked past the concert hall.
   b and then we went for a drink in the interval.
13 I noticed a strange man taking photographs of the empty house ☐
14 I noticed a strange man take photographs of the empty house ☐
   a and drive away in a red sports car.
   b while I was taking the dog for a walk.

Review and consolidation unit 4

Futures (1)

1 Tick (✓) the best option (a or b) to complete each sentence.

1 Elisa's so upset – she's on the verge of
   a leave her husband. ☐
   b leaving her husband. ☐

2 Look at the damage on these tyres –
   a they aren't going to last much longer. ☐
   b they aren't lasting much longer. ☐

3 I'm not very thirsty –
   a I think I won't have anything to drink. ☐
   b I don't think I'll have anything to drink. ☐

4 David's such a good engineer – he's bound
   a to get the job. ☐
   b get the job. ☐

5 Tania's just given me the tickets –
   a we're sitting in the front row. ☐
   b we're going to sit in the front row. ☐

6 That young pianist seems so talented –
   a I believe he'll win the competition. ☐
   b I believe he's winning the competition. ☐

Future Perfect and Future Continuous

2 Complete the sentences using a Future Perfect or Future Continuous form of a verb from the box. Use the pronoun *you* if necessary.

> ask   finish   watch   repair   sunbathe
> travel   clean   visit

1 Maria _____ all the rooms by the time the guests arrive.

2 By this time next week _____ on a beach in the Maldives.

3 _____ your brother play football on Saturday?

4 Do you think the engineer _____ my computer by this afternoon?

5 By the end of the journey she _____ more than 20,000 miles.

6 _____ preparing those figures in time for the directors' meeting?

7 _____ your half-sister while you're in the US?

8 During the lunch break tomorrow I _____ everyone to fill in a special questionnaire.

Verb patterns: *-ing* forms and infinitives

3 Complete the sentences with appropriate forms of verbs from the box.

> clean   drink   eat   feel   help   lock   meet
> speak   take   use

1 Will they allow us _____ our bikes on the train?

2 Danny agreed _____ me choose a new mobile.

3 Although it isn't good for me, I'm going to carry on _____ as much chocolate as I want!

4 Allie agreed _____ me outside the cinema at seven o'clock.

5 As we drove away from the house, I noticed Mrs Bolton _____ her windows.

6 We work in the same office – I can't avoid _____ to her.

7 I arranged _____ my brother's computer while mine was being repaired.

8 Once she got used to her new surroundings Lizzie stopped _____ homesick.

9 If you can't sleep, try _____ hot milk before you go to bed – that often helps.

10 Remember _____ the door tonight – we don't want to be burgled!

4 Tick (✓) the best explanation (a or b).

1 I regret telling Claudia the news.
   a I feel sorry about something I said in the past. ☐
   b I am about to tell Claudia some bad news. ☐

2 We stopped buying petrol.
   a We stopped the car and bought some petrol. ☐
   b We bought a new electric car. ☐

3 I tried painting the wall.
   a I was attempting to cover up a damp patch. ☐
   b I couldn't reach high enough to paint it all. ☐

4 Do you remember taking the tablets?
   a I am asking you about the past. ☐
   b I am reminding you to do something in the future. ☐

5 I stopped to eat.
   a I was full up. ☐
   b I was hungry. ☐

6 Dariusz tried to start the car.
   a It had broken down. ☐
   b He wanted to know if the engine was still making a strange noise. ☐

Personality traits for jobs

5 Use the clues to complete the crossword.

Across

1 She loves company. She's a _____ person.
4 He knows how to get the _____ out of people.
5 Dan's an accountant so he's good with _____.
10 I like company. I work well in a _____ .
12 You must be able to meet _____ deadlines.
14 He enjoys his work. He gets a lot of job _____ .

Down

1 Doctors follow a very strict career _____ .
2 I'm going to take a year _____ between jobs.
3 It wasn't just a job, it was a _____ of love.
6 Candidates must use their own _____ .
7 He's very precise. He has a real eye for _____ .
8 Ana's very sympathetic. She's a good _____ .
9 You must always keep calm under _____ .
11 I want workers with a 'can-do' _____ .
13 I'm fed up at work. It's time for a _____ of career.

Work

6 Choose the correct words in *italics*.

1 Miranda does *not-paid/voluntary* work for a local children's charity.
2 I work hard but I'm not a *working-centred/workaholic*.
3 Most people find *commuting/commute* tiring.
4 Employers have a duty to create a healthy *work-location/workplace*.
5 It's difficult to survive without some kind of *earn/ paid* employment.
6 I'm glad I don't live in a country with a *work-centred/workaholic* culture.
7 With modern means of communication, it's easy to work from *home/house*.
8 Our company is going to introduce *an adaptable/ a flexible* working day from next month.

Verb phrases about time

7 Choose the correct option for each gap (a, b or c).

1 I wanted to finish the essay by this morning but I _____ of time.
   a lost   b ran out   c ran over
2 When I'm bored I _____ the time by playing games on my computer.
   a lose   b take   c pass
3 If you want to _____ you should cycle to work – it's much faster.
   a save time   b save the time   c fast time
4 There's no rush – you can _____ time.
   a make your   b take the   c take your
5 We had some time _____ before the show so we went for a coffee.
   a to give up   b to kill   c to die
6 However busy you are, it's important to _____ time for your family and friends.
   a spend   b pass   c make

Collocations with prepositions

8 Find the mistakes in this blog and correct them.

I think one of the most important things in life is being happy at work. I'm a website designer and I remember that when I applied to my current job I told the interviewer I wasn't just keen of design, I was passionate on it! Perhaps that's one of the reasons I got the job. I suppose I'm quite lucky because not only do I love my work, I also get on really well with my colleagues. They are all very different at me, but we all believe to what we are doing, so there's a great team spirit in the office. I work for a big advertising agency. It's a very busy and competitive business. Some of my colleagues worry of that but I just get on and do my work. I think I'm pretty good of what I do and I'm really proud in some of the work I've done for the company.

How to...

9 Complete the dialogue with words from the box.

believe   about   do   fact   sure   possibility

A: I'm thinking (1) _____ applying for a job abroad.
B: Really? Where exactly?
A: Well, I'm not (2) _____ yet but one (3) _____ would be the States.
B: Is that realistic? (4) _____ me, I think you'll find it very difficult to get a work permit for the US, I really (5) _____ .
A: That's true for most people. But the (6) _____ is I have some cousins over there, so they could probably help me.

Reading

1 **a** Read the article and choose the best title (1–3).

1 Newspapers' Deadly Rival

2 Blogging Websites

3 The Internet News Millionaire

b Read the article again. Write true (T) or false (F).

1 Drudge calls himself 'the ultimate blogger'. ☐

2 He loved news and current affairs, even as a child. ☐

3 He was a journalist for *The Washington Star*. ☐

4 The Internet didn't exist when Drudge was a child. ☐

5 Drudge got his news from talking to people. ☐

6 He interviewed Monica Lewinsky in 1998. ☐

7 The *Drudge Report* is very useful for people who want up-to-date news. ☐

8 Matt Drudge doesn't think the Internet will take over from newspapers in the future. ☐

c Find the phrases from the box in the article and match them with the meanings (1–10).

> sprung up   stems from   fanatical obsession
> dead-end jobs   sifting through   inside stories
> juiciest gossip   breaking news
> a 'must-see' resource   news junkie

1 things that are happening now

_____

2 someone who wants to know the latest news all the time

_____

3 looking very carefully at all the details to find something

_____

4 an overriding interest in something

_____

5 began/originated with

_____

6 very useful or valuable place to find things

_____

7 information from people who are involved in actual events

_____

8 work that has no future and doesn't lead to a career

_____

9 appeared from nowhere

_____

10 exciting or shocking scandal

_____

(1) This is Matt Drudge, millionaire founder and owner of the *Drudge Report*, the first and most successful online 'newspaper'. People have called Drudge the ultimate blogger but he doesn't accept  the description. He considers the *Drudge Report* to be a proper newspaper, very different from the thousands of weblogs which have sprung up on the Internet.

(2) Drudge's fascination for news and gossip stems from a childhood job delivering papers for *The Washington Star*. It gave him plenty of time and opportunity to catch up with the latest news. Uninterested in school work or sport, Drudge developed a fanatical obsession with rumours and political gossip. At school his only good grades were for current affairs. Following a series of dead-end jobs, Drudge ended up in Los Angeles in the 1990s, just in time for the beginning of what was to become the Internet.

(3) The fledgling World Wide Web was a fertile hunting ground for Drudge. He spent hours sifting through the newsgroups and rudimentary websites that then existed, searching for rumours and inside stories from the political and entertainment worlds. He launched the *Drudge Report* website in 1995, a daily 'rumour bulletin' containing his version of the latest and juiciest gossip from Hollywood and Washington. Always managing to be the first with breaking news, Drudge's success was assured when he became the first person to publicise the Monica Lewinsky scandal in 1998. The website became so popular that in 2006, Drudge was named one of the 100 most influential people in the world by *Time* magazine.

(4) Now with a turnover of over $1 million a year and many thousands of subscribers, the *Drudge Report* has become a 'must-see' resource for those hungry for the latest news and gossip. But will the ever-increasing availability of news on the Internet mean the end for its older rival, the conventional newspaper? Drudge doesn't think so. He sees the two working together. As far as the news junkie Drudge is concerned, there can never be too much news ...

Grammar | conditional structures (1)

2 Write conditional sentences starting with *If*. Be careful with modal verbs.

(First Conditional)

I hope he asks me to marry him because I'd accept.

If he asks me to marry him, I'll accept.

1   I'm planning to get a laptop so I can send emails when I'm travelling.

_____

2   I don't want to be late for my interview so I hope the train comes on time.

_____

3   Maribel hopes to pass the driving test because she wants to buy a car.

_____

(Second Conditional)

The government wants to build more roads but they don't have enough money.

If the government had more money, it would build more roads.

4   I'd like to swim more but I don't live near a pool.

_____

5   Terry would like to travel around the world but he's scared of flying.

_____

6   Celia's dream is to join a choir but unfortunately she can't sing.

_____

(Third Conditional)

I met him because I went to the party.

If I hadn't gone to the party, I wouldn't have met him.

7   Dave won because he knew all the answers.

_____

8   Helena didn't go to the concert because she lost the tickets.

_____

9   Malik might have got a promotion but his sales figures were disappointing.

_____

10 We had to queue up for tickets so we missed the start of the show.

_____

(Mixed conditionals)

11 Malcolm isn't at university now because he didn't get good marks in his exams.

_____

12 My parents aren't rich so they didn't buy me expensive presents.

_____

3 Complete the dialogue using appropriate conditional forms of the verbs in brackets.

Ann: Excuse me. I (1) _____ (like) to report a stolen handbag.

Officer: Of course, madam. Let me take some details. Your name?

Ann: Mrs Ann Kendall.

Officer: And where and when did this happen?

Ann: At Denham's department store, about 20 minutes ago. I put my bag down while I was paying at the register ...

Officer: And someone took your bag?

Ann: Exactly. If I'd been paying attention, it (2) _____ (not happen).

Officer: Any idea who did it?

Ann: Not really. If there (3) _____ (be) anyone suspicious, I would have noticed.

Officer: Are there any security cameras in that store?

Ann: I don't think so. If there were any cameras the staff (4) _____ (tell) me.

Officer: And what was in the bag?

Ann: Everything. My mobile phone, keys ...

Officer: Any credit cards?

Ann: Yes, one. The thief might try to use it.

Officer: Well, if you (5) _____ (phone) your credit card company now, you (6) _____ (be able) to cancel the cards before anyone can use them.

Ann: OK. But what about my keys? The thief might be able to get into my house.

Officer: Was there anything in your bag that had your address on it, like a driving licence?

Ann: No, I don't think so.

Officer: If the thief (7) _____ (not have) your address, he (8) _____ (not know) where you live, will he?

Ann: No, I suppose not. Do you think there's any chance of me getting the bag back?

Officer: It's hard to say, but if anybody (9) _____ (find) the bag, we (10) _____ (contact) you.

Reading

1 **a** Read the advertisement. Who is it mainly aimed at?

1 people who play extreme sports ☐
2 people who might like to try extreme sports ☐
3 people who want to improve their physical fitness ☐

b Read the advertisement again and answer the questions.

1 How many extreme sports are mentioned by name in the text?
_____

2 What two things can you get from the website?
_____

3 Is the weekend suitable for people who aren't physically fit?
_____

4 How many extreme sports were available last year?
_____

5 How much do tickets cost if you buy them at the event itself?
_____

c Match words or phrases in the advertisement with the meanings.

1 an opportunity to make something imaginary come true
_____

2 most important and talented
_____

3 having a strong desire to do something _____

4 well protected _____

5 extremely exciting
_____

6 boring, always the same
_____

7 when you know what will happen _____

8 teachers of physical skills
_____

How much danger can you take?
Join us for *National Extreme Sports Weekend* and find out!

- Have you ever watched snowboarders and mountain bikers and thought, 'I could do that'?
- Are you tired of the humdrum daily routine and ready to challenge yourself?
- Are you longing for some real risk in your predictable everyday life?

Well, now is your chance to turn fantasy into thrilling reality ...

This year *National Extreme Sports Weekend* is better than ever. We are offering you the chance to try out over fifty different extreme sports, twice as many as previous years. 100 leading instructors from around the world are waiting to share their top tips and closely-guarded secrets. And you don't even need to be super fit, we have something for everyone!

abseiling   canoeing
windsurfing
skateboarding   in-line skating
snowboarding
free running   paragliding

Are you ready for the risk of a lifetime?
Are you ready for the challenge?
If you don't come, you'll never know!

National Extreme Sports Weekend is at Fairfield Park, Birmingham, 21–22 July.
Tickets and a full schedule of events available from www.NatExsports.com.
£20 on the day, £15 in advance.

Grammar | advice and permission

2 Complete the dialogue.

Doctor: So, what brings you to the surgery today?

Patient: I'm just feeling rather lethargic and lacking in energy. I thought you might have some useful advice for me.

Doctor: Right. (1) _____ I ask you about exercise? Do you do any?

Patient: Not really. I just sit around in the office or at home most of the time.

Doctor: Well, you (2) _____ do that. If I (3) _____ you, I'd join a gym or a sports team.

Patient: I'm not very keen on sport.

Doctor: What about swimming?

Patient: Oh, I can't swim. When I was a child I wasn't (4) _____ to have swimming lessons because my parents thought it was too dangerous.

Doctor: That's a pity. They should (5) _____ taught you to swim when you were young; it's much easier than when you're grown up. What about your habits – do you smoke?

Patient: Yes, I do. But only at home in the evenings – we (6) _____ allowed to smoke at work.

Doctor: Well, you (7) _____ really try to give up. Now, what about diet?

Patient: I don't like cooking very much. I usually eat take-aways.

Doctor: If I were you, I (8) _____ do that too often. It's much better to buy fresh food and cook it yourself.

Vocabulary | sport

4 Choose the correct words in *italics*.

1 The best way to protect your head is to wear a *harness/helmet*.

2 When is the team going to start *training/studying* for the Olympics?

3 I'm very *competitive/addictive* – I always want to win!

4 By law, all commercial ships must carry a supply of *wetsuits/lifejackets* in case of emergencies.

5 There is nothing more exciting than white-water *swimming/rafting*.

6 Ice hockey players usually wear thick *gloves/goggles* to protect their hands.

7 Taking part *of/in* team sports is healthy as well as fun.

8 There were more than 50,000 *participants/spectators* at the recent football match between Brazil and Italy.

Pronunciation | connected speech (3)

5 **a** Look at the underlined part of each sentence and write 'weak form', 'w', 'j' or 'r'.

1 Could I ask <u>you about</u> exercise? _____

2 You shouldn't <u>have</u> eaten those cakes! _____

3 I usually shave <u>after I've</u> had a shower. _____

4 Are we allowed <u>to</u> park here? _____

5 She's always <u>happy and</u> cheerful in warm weather. _____

b 🔵 15 Listen and check your answers. Then repeat the sentences.

3 Complete the speech bubbles using the word in brackets.

1 You _____ in here. (allowed)

2 You _____ so fast. (shouldn't)

3 In those days, women _____ trousers to work. (couldn't)

4 You _____ a coat! (have)

5 If I _____ shoes with such high heels. (were)

6 We _____ – it's going to be hot this weekend. (should)

Listening

1 a 🔊 16 Cover the audioscript. Listen to the dialogue and choose the correct answer.

The friends are talking about ...

1 their favourite film stars. ☐
2 film stars who do their own stunts. ☐
3 the role of stunt men in recent films. ☐

b Listen again and tick (✓) the correct column in the table.

	Daniel Craig	Matt Damon	Pierce Brosnan	Sean Connery
has done his own stunts				
didn't do stunts				
jumped off a building				
did martial arts training				
was in a James Bond movie				
is American				

c Find the words from the box in the audioscript and match them with the meanings (1–8).

> action sequences special effects fake documentary
> maimed role martial arts tougher

1 sports such as judo, karate and kung fu _____
2 a film which gives facts about real events _____
3 so seriously injured that part of your body is permanently damaged _____
4 a character in a film or play _____
5 techniques which allow films to show things that didn't actually happen _____
6 stronger, braver _____
7 parts of a film containing exciting scenes of fighting, car chases, etc. _____
8 pretend, not real _____

AUDIOSCRIPT

Lee: Wow. That was a great film. I loved all those action sequences.

Sue: Yeah, and Daniel Craig makes a great action hero!

Lee: And (1) _____ athletic – the way he jumped off that building ...

Sue: Oh, I'm sure that wasn't him. They always use stunt men for that sort of thing.

Lee: No, no. He did the stunts himself. I read all about it.

Sue: Well, it (2) _____ look like he was doing it all himself. But you can't tell these days, can you? I mean with all the special effects they have now. It could all have been done on a computer.

Lee: But it never looks the same. You can always tell if something's fake.

Sue: Maybe, but surely they wouldn't allow a film star to do anything that's, like, really dangerous. Suppose they got maimed or killed?

Lee: I think it used to be like that. I know Sean Connery never did any stunts in the early James Bond films. He was (3) _____ a big star they couldn't take the risk of him being seriously injured.

Sue: Or Pierce Brosnan. I remember seeing this documentary about a famous stunt man called Gary Powell – he did all the stunts for Brosnan in his Bond movies.

Lee: I know that name. (4) _____ was Gary Powell who trained Daniel Craig.

Sue: Really? What do you mean, 'trained'?

Lee: Craig had to do three months of physical training to prepare for his Bond role.

Sue: So, is Daniel Craig the only film star that does his own stunts?

Lee: Oh no, quite a few of them do it now.

Sue: What about the American actor, Matt Damon? There are some great action sequences in *The Bourne Ultimatum*.

Lee: Yes, he (5) _____ do his own stunts in the Jason Bourne films. Apparently he did 12 weeks of martial arts to prepare for the part. And I think Tom Cruise did a lot of the stunts in *Mission Impossible*.

Sue: Well, I'm surprised. Film actors these days seem to be a tougher lot than I'd thought ...

Grammar | emphasis

2 Read the audioscript again and write *does, did, so, such* or *it* in the gaps.

3 Rewrite the sentences using an appropriate form of *do* to make them emphatic.

1 I like your new suit.

   _____

2 Amanda complains a lot.

   _____

3 He said he was sorry several times.

   _____

4 I asked the boss for permission.

   _____

5 We know what we are talking about.

   _____

4 Choose the correct words in *italics*.

1 That was *such a/such* beautiful music.
2 Their new house was *so/such* expensive.
3 The cotton suit is *so/such* much cheaper than the silk one.
4 *Million Dollar Baby* was *such/so* a good film.
5 There are so *much/many* beautiful beaches in this region.
6 Clint Eastwood is *such/so* fantastic in that role.
7 His sister is *so/such* a beautiful girl, don't you agree?
8 We're older now so we don't go out *so/such* often.

5 Write responses to each statement, emphasising the phrase in brackets.

I hear you can't stand her new flatmate. (her new boyfriend)

No, it's her new boyfriend that I can't stand.

1 I believe they love Japanese food. (Chinese food)
   No, it's _____

2 Apparently she spoke to his partner. (his assistant)
   No, it's _____

3 So you don't like the second film? (the first film)
   No, it's _____

4 Does your finger hurt? (my thumb)
   No, it's _____

5 Is it true that Clara really doesn't like modern drama? (modern poetry)
   No, it's _____

6 I hear you don't like his behaviour. (his attitude)
   No, it's _____

Pronunciation | stress: emphasis (1)

6 a Underline the word which has the strongest stress in the sentences.

1 The children did behave themselves.
2 She's such a lovely person.
3 We do love Hollywood movies.
4 That old computer is so slow.
5 It was Jane that wanted to see you.

b 🔵 17 Listen and check.

Vocabulary | phrasal verbs with *out*

7 a Choose the correct words in *italics*.

1 I wasn't able to *find/give* out what time the film starts.
2 You'll have to use another printer. This one's *run/sorted* out of ink.
3 It was hard work but it *fell/turned* out alright in the end.
4 Mel, please *give/take* out a copy to everyone in class 3C.
5 Jim's going to *sort/find* out the files.

b Four of the sentences contain mistakes. Find the mistakes and correct them.

1 We weren't sure about the babysitter but she took out to be really good.
2 Dan's had to go to the gym on his own since he fell out with his gym partner.
3 My car broke down last week and the mechanic wasn't able to put it out.
4 I'm afraid we only give out catalogues to established clients.
5 Make sure you fall out your cigarettes before you enter the building.
6 If I have a problem with my house, my neighbour turns it out – he's a builder.

How to... | talk about which film to watch

8 Complete the sentences using suitable phrases from the box. Two of the phrases are not needed.

> based on   a hard time   judging by   looks like
> the sound of   sounds like   sounds a bit

1 He's a good actor, but I have _____ seeing him as an action hero.
2 _____ the cover, it looks good.
3 I like _____ the title, it's intriguing.
4 I think it might be interesting – it's _____ a true story.
5 A film about boxing – that _____ boring.

Conditional structures (1)

1 Choose the correct options to complete the sentences.

1 If Steven hadn't passed the exam, he _____ to university.
   a didn't go   **b** wouldn't go
   c wouldn't have gone

2 If you _____ some ice in a drink, it makes it cooler.
   a have put   **b** put   **c** will put

3 I _____ for the cinema if you pay for the restaurant.
   a paid   **b** 'll pay   **c** am paying

4 If you _____ a positive attitude, you won't succeed in business.
   a don't have   **b** didn't have   **c** haven't had

5 What _____ if your car broke down on the motorway?
   a will you do   **b** would you do
   c are you doing

6 I _____ by taxi if I were you.
   a 'd go   **b** must go   **c** will go

7 If John got a pay rise, we might _____ to a bigger apartment.
   a have moved   **b** be moving   **c** move

8 They wouldn't _____ that hotel if they'd known how expensive it was.
   a chose   **b** have chosen   **c** choose

9 I would _____ lots of money now if I'd got that promotion.
   a have earned   **b** earning   **c** be earning

10 If Dexter _____ a car he would have collected them from the airport.
   a had   **b** would have   **c** will have

Advice and permission

2 Add one word to each sentence.

      have
You shouldn't ⁄ spoken to him like that.

1 In the 19th century, women allowed to become members of the British parliament.

2 If I were you, I wouldn't wasted so much time on the Internet.

3 Excuse me. I use your mobile phone to make a short call? Mine isn't working.

4 You believe everything politicians say – they rarely tell the whole truth.

5 We were lucky. When we were young we stay out all day playing in the fields around my grandmother's house.

6 I'm sorry but you aren't to come in here unless you wear a jacket and tie.

7 Once you have provided us with a valid email address you use our software free of charge.

8 Where are the potatoes? You bought some when you went shopping this morning.

Emphasis

3 Put the words in order to make emphatic sentences.
that / the children / go there / It / want to / is
It is the children that want to go there.

1 made me / It was / feel sick / that / the shellfish
_____

2 try / She / you / did / to contact
_____

3 do / do voluntary work / I / who / admire people
_____

4 is / It / my / injured / is / left leg / that
_____

5 such a / footballer / Gerald / good / is
_____

6 money / give / She / a lot of / to charity / does
_____

7 that / It / mobile phone / was stolen / was / my
_____

8 exciting / Yesterday's / so / football match / was
_____

9 do / Javier / did / work / a lot of / for us
_____

10 does / the housework / It / his wife / is / that
_____

4 Complete the sentences with words from the box.

is	so	that	such	do	does	did	it

1 It is John's children _____ I feel sorry for.
2 I think Sylvia really _____ love him.
3 That flat screen television is _____ expensive.
4 _____ was Liz that I was trying to contact.
5 I _____ try to get front row seats but they were sold out.
6 The children _____ like you, I promise!
7 Clare is _____ a wonderful mother.
8 It _____ the final episode I want you to record.

Risk and achievement

5 Complete the sentences with words from the box. One of the words is not needed.

> risk gamble opportunity chance stake
> ambition substantial

1 I'm very glad that I had the _____ to travel when I was young.
2 When I was a child it was my _____ to become an astronaut.
3 Our company made a lot of money this year so we're expecting a _____ pay rise.
4 Although I knew it was a _____ , I invested all my money in my best friend's new shop.
5 If we don't win this contract our company's future will be at _____ .
6 Talk to him now. You might never get another _____ .

Challenge and sport

6 Match the sentence beginnings (1–12) with the sentence endings (a–l).

1 There's nothing I enjoy more than facing ☐
2 Mario put all his efforts ☐
3 Our trainer wants us to focus ☐
4 It took a lot of courage for her to deal ☐
5 Carrie has spent years campaigning for ☐
6 He needs to run a lot faster if he wants to break ☐
7 Serious athletes have to put ☐
8 To become team captain, Chas had to battle ☐
9 It's necessary to be ☐
10 Due to injury, Caroline was unable to take ☐
11 He's about to begin training ☐
12 Completing the marathon gave Dieter a great ☐

a sense of achievement.
b against several strong competitors.
c competitive to excel at any sport.
d the record.
e part in the race.
f up with endless hours of training.
g for the Olympics.
h with all the dangers.
i on endurance rather than speed.
j a challenge.
k into finding a better job.
l the rights of indigenous peoples.

Phrasal verbs with *out*

7 Write phrasal verbs with *out* in the gaps.

1 I go to the gym every day and _____ .
2 Although the heat was intense, the firefighters managed to _____ the fire.
3 Excuse me, Alex. Could you _____ the time of the next train to Exeter?
4 Can you get me a few things at the shops? We've _____ of bread, coffee and milk.
5 Don't worry about tidying up – I'll help you _____ the mess.
6 We were good friends for years then suddenly, for no reason, we _____ .

Distances and dimensions

8 Use the clues to complete the crossword.

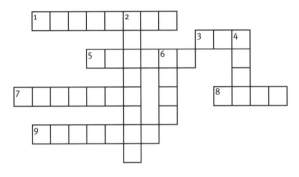

1 The curtains don't quite touch the ground; we need to _____ them by about ten inches.
2 They are going to _____ the bridge so that large trucks can pass underneath.
3 Temperatures can be quite _____ in winter.
4 How _____ is the gate? Will the car get through?
5 My husband's very tall so we're increasing the _____ of the doors in our house.
6 How _____ is Mount Everest?
7 He needs a large jacket because of the _____ of his shoulders.
8 Don't disturb her. She's _____ in thought.
9 The government is going to _____ the motorway from three lanes to four.

How to...

9 Choose the correct words in *italics*.

1 Excuse me, if I could *do/make* a point here …
2 This looks good, *judging/looking* by the cover.
3 I have a *complicated/hard* time seeing her as a romantic lead.
4 If you could let me *stop/ finish* my point.
5 'Dark Night' – I like the *sound/way* of that film.

Listening

1 a 🌐 18 Cover the audioscript. Listen to a radio interview and complete the table.

Work	US: *Joe makes feature films.*
	UK: (1) _____
Film-making	US: (2) _____
	UK: (3) _____
Shopping	US: (4) _____
	UK: (5) _____
Weather	US: (6) _____
	UK: *It was always cloudy.*

b Listen again and write questions for the answers (1–8).

How old was Joe when his parents gave him a movie camera?

about ten

1 _____
   _____

   five years

2 _____
   _____

   28

3 _____
   _____

   work

4 _____
   _____

   three

5 _____
   _____

   There is more money involved.

6 _____
   _____

   walking to the shops

7 _____
   _____

   Because of the enormous distances between places.

8 _____
   _____

   Because it was always so cloudy.

c Now read the audioscript. Match phrases with the meanings (1–5).

1 when people from many backgrounds mix together

2 managers of film companies

3 do something that irritates people

4 constantly supervising and watching somebody

5 making films in real places, not in studios

AUDIOSCRIPT

A: Hi everybody and welcome once again to *America – the Melting Pot*. This week we have as our guest the British film director, Joe Grendal. Welcome to the show, Joe.

B: Thanks. It's great to be here.

A: Now, you've been in the US for the last five years. Is that right?

B: Yeah. I came here when I was 28.

A: What made you choose to live in the States?

B: Well, work really. I had a reasonably successful career back in London, making TV commercials and short films, but I really wanted to get into feature films.

A: You made those famous commercials for trainers, didn't you?

B: Yes. I (1) _____ do lots of work for sportswear companies. Some of the commercials I made were shown in the States and that's really how the connection with Hollywood began. Some American studio executives saw my work on TV here and invited me over.

A: Were you always interested in movie-making?

B: I guess so. Certainly when I was a child I (2) _____ spend hours watching Hollywood movies on TV and my parents gave me a movie camera when I was about ten. I (3) _____ drive the family mad rushing around filming everything!

A: You've made three films over here now. How does film-making here compare to Britain?

B: It's not that different, really. But there's a lot more money involved. Back in the UK we (4) _____ have much contact with the accountants. But here they're on top of you all the time!

A: Do you find that difficult?

B: Well, let's just say I'm still (5) _____ it!

A: Is there anything you really miss from the old country?

B: For me, no. But my wife misses walking to the shops. The distances between places are so enormous here, so you have to drive everywhere. In London we had lots of local shops so we (6) _____ usually walk to get our shopping.

A: Yes. Nobody walks here. They go to the gym instead!

B: I know. People drive to the gym and then spend hours walking on the treadmills. Crazy!

A: Right! Er, the weather, surely that's very different here?

B: Sure. I love the sunny weather here in southern California. In fact, it means we can do a lot of location work. That's something new for me because it was always so cloudy in England we (7) _____ do much outdoors – I always preferred to be inside a nice warm studio!

A: What about the way we talk – the American accent ...

B: Oh, I (8) _____ that. It's probably more difficult for you lot to understand me. Although, I can't say I've really had any problems.

Grammar | *used to/would*

2 Look at the audioscript again. Write appropriate forms of *used to, be used to, get used to* or *would* in the gaps (1–8).

3 Tick (✓) the correct options. More than one option may be possible.

1 When I was a child I _____ play football all the time.
   a would ☐
   b got used to ☐
   c used to ☐

2 Gerald _____ be overweight.
   a used to ☐
   b would ☐
   c didn't use to ☐

3 We _____ go to bed early when we were small.
   a didn't use to ☐
   b would ☐
   c used to ☐

4 It took me ages to _____ this new diet.
   a get use to ☐
   b get used to ☐
   c getting used to ☐

5 _____ that new computer?
   a Are you getting used to ☐
   b Do you get used to ☐
   c Are you used to ☐

6 _____ be in the school swimming team?
   a Are they used to ☐
   b Did they use to ☐
   c Didn't they use to ☐

7 Do you think she _____ living on her own?
   a gets used to ☐
   b will get used to ☐
   c is used to ☐

8 Our youngest child _____ watch television for hours on end.
   a would ☐
   b used to ☐
   c was used to ☐

9 _____ live in the countryside before you came here?
   a Do you get used to ☐
   b Did you use to ☐
   c Would you ☐

10 _____ driving on the right?
   a Do you used to ☐
   b Are you getting used to ☐
   c Are you use to ☐

Vocabulary | appearance

4 Use the clues to complete the crossword.

Across

2 a type of hair that isn't straight
4 top models are like this
8 graceful and attractive
9 a type of hair, but not straight
10 no hair

Down

1 Arnold Schwarzenegger
2 old people have these on their faces
3 not a natural hair colour
5 light brown
6 you're like this if you sunbathe
7 not slim, not fat, not tall

Pronunciation | consonant clusters (1)

5 a Think about the consonant clusters at the start of each word. Which word is the odd-one out in each group?

1 *scruffy/scrape/squash*
2 *straight/stocky/string*
3 *slippery/slim/splash*
4 *swim/sphere/sweet*
5 *spiky/splash/splendid*
6 *smile/smoke/snow*

b 🔊 19 Listen and check your answers.

Reading

1 a Read the short story quickly and choose the best title.

1 The Swiss Burglar
2 Driving in Milan
3 The Disastrous Holiday

Kirsten and Dieter were very excited about their driving holiday in Italy. They packed their convertible car with three suitcases and set off from their home early in the morning. The weather was warm and, as they drove across the Swiss border into Italy, they lowered the roof and enjoyed the pleasant sensation of the warm spring air rushing past their heads.

By the middle of the afternoon they had reached Milan. Kirsten wasn't very good at map-reading but she was sure they could make their way to the centre of the city, find a parking space and enjoy a delicious late lunch at a local restaurant. As they drove into one of the city's quiet suburbs they suddenly heard a loud bang and felt something crash into the back of their car. Turning around they saw a small motorbike lying on its side behind their car with two young men sprawled on the road beside it. Dieter stopped the car and jumped out to see if he could help. One of the young men was groaning loudly. Kirsten knew how to give first aid so she opened her door and approached the groaning man. Suddenly the two men jumped up and rushed towards the car. In less than two seconds they had leapt into the car and driven off at high speed, leaving Dieter and Kirsten standing in the street.

Dieter started shouting for help in German. But there was no one around to hear him. At first Kirsten wasn't too worried. She couldn't speak Italian either, but she was sure they'd manage to find a police station nearby. After half an hour of walking they had still failed to find a police officer or anyone to help them and they began to get more worried. Their passports, credit cards, mobile phones and money had all been in the car and Dieter was worried that the thieves might be using his credit cards to go on a massive spending spree.

About 20 minutes later they saw a police car driving along the street and they rushed into the road to flag it down. Dieter tried to explain what had happened to the police officer. But the officer couldn't understand German and decided to take the two

Swiss tourists back to the police station. He was sure one of his colleagues would be able to translate for them. Unfortunately as he was driving back to the police station there was an emergency call on his radio and he was instructed to drive to the scene of a serious accident. Dieter and Kirsten were forced to sit in the back of the police car for another two hours while the officer dealt with the emergency.

By the time they arrived at the local police station it was eight o'clock in the evening and they were exhausted. Using the police station's phone, Dieter succeeded in contacting his credit card company to cancel his cards. Once they'd done this they decided the best thing was to get home as quickly as possible. A police officer drove them to the railway station and lent them the money to buy two tickets. They just managed to catch the last train – the slow overnight service back home.

Relieved to be on their way home, the couple soon fell asleep. They woke at seven in the morning as the train pulled into the station. With no money for a taxi, they were forced to walk back to their house. Just as they turned into their street they saw a large removal truck leaving. Kirsten was surprised; she didn't think any of their neighbours were moving house. As they approached their house they noticed the front door was open. Running into the house, Dieter gasped with shock. The house was completely empty. Then he remembered. Their house keys had been on the same ring as the car key …

b Read the story again and number the events (a–l) in the correct order.

a   Two Italian men drive off. ☐

b   They have to wait while the police officer deals with an accident. ☐

c   They catch the slow train back home. ☐

d   Dieter and Kirsten leave. ☐

e   They get into an Italian police car. ☐

f   Dieter and Kirsten get back to their house. ☐

g   They get out of their car to see what has happened. ☐

h   The Italian men steal everything from their house and drive away in a van. ☐

i   They walk around trying to find a police station. ☐

j   The police take Dieter and Kirsten to the railway station. ☐

k   They drive into the suburbs of Milan. ☐

l   A motorbike crashes into the back of their car. ☐

c Match words and phrases in the story to the meanings (1–10).

1   a car with an opening roof _____

2   left on a journey _____

3   moving quickly _____

4   lying with legs and arms spread out _____

5   making noises as if in pain _____

6   spending a large amount of money at one time _____

7   signal a car or taxi to stop _____

8   very tired _____

9   gave something to somebody but they have to repay it later _____

10   a large vehicle used to move furniture _____

Grammar | wishes and regrets

2 Rewrite the sentences using the words in brackets.

I regret that I was so lazy. (only)

If only I hadn't been so lazy.

1   I regret not going to university. (wish)

_____

2   I wanted to buy an extra copy but they had sold out. (going)

_____

3   Ali didn't bring his computer so he couldn't read his emails. (if)

_____

4   I regret that I didn't spend more time studying. (only)

_____

5   We didn't like the hotel so we didn't enjoy our stay. (would've)

_____

6   I wish I hadn't left the party so early. (regret)

_____

7   I planned to stay there longer but my visa ran out. (was)

_____

8   I wish I'd paid more attention to my tutor's advice. (not paying)

_____

Pronunciation | wishes and regrets

3 🔊 20 Listen and check your answers to exercise 2. Then repeat the sentences.

How to... | reminisce about the past

4 Look at the photograph and read the text. There are four factual errors. Find the mistakes and correct them.

This photo really brings back memories of my childhood holidays. We used to go to the seaside in the winter. Although the weather was often too hot, I remember that we always had a lot of fun. We would spend hours swimming in the sea and playing games on the beach. I loved building sand castles and my sisters used to bury my legs in the sand! We spent most of the time laughing and playing tricks on each other. My parents loved driving along the coast, stopping to have picnics in the forest. I would sit with my three sisters and my mother. My father would serve us drinks and food from a picnic basket. Everything got covered in sand but it still tasted delicious! Yes, I often get nostalgic for those days when I see photos of the seaside.

Vocabulary | feelings

1 Match the statements (1–8) with adjectives from the box.

> annoyed   confused   curious
> excited   relieved   sceptical
> shocked   suspicious

1 Thank goodness you're safe. I was so worried about you! _____

2 I wonder what's in that box? I'd love to have a look inside. _____

3 What on earth are we supposed to do? I really can't understand these instructions. _____

4 Wow! Front row seats for the concert! I can't wait! _____

5 His behaviour gets on my nerves. He's so rude! _____

6 I don't trust our new boss. I think he wants to get rid of me. _____

7 €500 for a single pair of shoes? That's outrageous! _____

8 The doctor said I should lose weight but he doesn't know what he's talking about. _____

2 Choose the correct words in *italics*.

1 Sarah doesn't like football or tennis. In fact, she's pretty *uninterested/ uneasy* in sports in general.

2 The children got very *excited/curious* when I told them we were going to Disneyland next summer.

3 I'll get a good grade; I'm always *optimistic/sceptical* about tests.

4 Clive's very *relieved/uneasy* about making the presentation – the idea of standing up in front of a group of people always worries him.

5 They're quite *uninterested/suspicious* about their new neighbour. He seems to do a lot of strange things in the middle of the night.

6 We were very *relieved/uneasy* when we heard that nobody had been hurt in the car crash.

Reading

3 **a** Read the newspaper article. Complete the gaps with the extracts (a–e). Two are not needed.

a it was exciting

b it is important

c It seems strange that

d It's good that

e It was clear that

The Musician with no Memory

Police in Sheerness, Kent have appealed for help in identifying a mystery man who was found wandering on a beach two days ago.

The mystery man seems unable to speak or write and may not even understand English. When he was picked up by the police he was smartly dressed in a suit and tie, but the labels were missing and he had no documents on him. It had been raining and his clothes were soaking wet. (1) [_____] although the man had no obvious physical injuries, he was confused and disoriented. He is white and in his 20s or early 30s.

The man was taken to Medway Maritime Hospital and put under the supervision of Michael Camp, a local social worker. The mystery deepened when nurses at the hospital gave the man a pen and paper and, rather than writing his name and address, he drew a picture of a grand piano. There is a piano in the hospital's chapel and Mr Camp took the man there. He proceeded to sit down and play classical music for two hours non-stop. (2) [_____] the man was an expert pianist – onlookers described his performance as 'virtuoso'. Staff at the hospital dubbed him 'The Piano Man'.

Kent Police believe the man may be a professional musician who is suffering from amnesia after some kind of traumatic accident. Others think he may be a con artist or an illegal immigrant from Eastern Europe. Photos and a description of the man have been circulated around Europe's police forces.

In order to know how to treat the man, doctors say (3) [_____] to establish his identity and medical history.

Anyone who thinks they may be able to identify this man is asked to get in touch with the National Missing Persons Helpline.

b Read the article again and answer the questions.

1 Who found the mystery man?

_____

_____

2 What was suspicious about the man's clothes?

_____

_____

3 Why did the social worker take the man to the hospital chapel?

_____

_____

4 What made the police think the man might be a professional musician?

_____

_____

5 Why has the man's description been circulated around Europe, and not just in the UK?

_____

_____

6 Who do you think the mystery man is? Why?

_____

_____

c Find the words and phrases from the box in the article and match them with the meanings (1–10).

> appealed   wandering   disoriented   chapel
> non-stop   dubbed   virtuoso   amnesia
> traumatic   con artist   immigrant   circulated

1 gave someone a special name _____

2 someone who makes money from tricking people _____

3 an illness in which you lose your memory _____

4 asked for assistance _____

5 extremely stressful _____

6 confused about where you are/what you are doing _____

7 continuously _____

8 walking around without a purpose _____

9 showing the highest level of skill and talent _____

10 a room for religious ceremonies _____

11 make something move around _____

12 a person who has come to live in a different country _____

Grammar | preparatory *it*

4 Complete the sentences with words and phrases from the box.

> clear   my intention   no use   seems
> was exciting   was good   was sad   worth

1 It's _____ talking to her about it, she never listens to anyone.

2 It's _____ to study medicine one day.

3 It _____ that they are not going to give us a refund.

4 It's _____ that if you eat less, you will lose weight.

5 It _____ to meet my favourite film star in person.

6 It _____ of you to help us with our application forms.

7 It's _____ saving up for something you really want.

8 It _____ to hear about the terrible famine in Africa.

5 Find the mistakes in five of these sentences and correct them.

1 It's no use that relying on him, he's not very trustworthy.

2 It seems that the post hasn't arrived this morning. How annoying!

3 It important is not to tell anyone your credit card PIN number.

4 It's always good to getting a second opinion when you want to buy something expensive.

5 It's my intention to complain about your behaviour to the manager.

6 It's worth paying a little extra to get shoes that will really last.

7 It a real pleasure was to meet your parents at last.

8 It was strange that to see so many new faces at the youth club.

Review and consolidation unit 6

used to/would

1 Rewrite the sentences using the words in brackets.

He doesn't swim in the sea any more. (used)

He used to swim in the sea.

1 Are you becoming accustomed to life in the big city? (getting)

_____

2 Sally didn't have any friends when she was a child. (use)

_____

3 I went to the library every morning when I was a student. (would)

_____

4 The company doesn't export cars to Asia any longer. (used)

_____

5 Did he become familiar with the software quickly? (get)

_____

6 When I was young I didn't watch much television. (use)

_____

7 How often did you get the bus to school? (would)

_____

8 I've become accustomed to staying up late. (got)

_____

9 It was easy to become familiar with the computer. (used)

_____

10 Pepe lives in a big house now. (didn't)

_____

Wishes and regrets

2 What are the people saying? Complete the sentences using the words in brackets.

1 Jamie's sad because he forgot to send Maria a birthday card. (going)

'I _____ , but I forgot.'

2 Carmela is upset because she woke up late and missed the bus. (only)

'_____ , then I wouldn't have missed the bus.'

3 Didier is unhappy because he couldn't get a ticket to the concert. (wish)

'I _____ been able to get a ticket.'

4 Miles didn't go to Sally's party because he had a headache. (would've)

'If I _____ gone to Sally's party.'

5 Isabel is sad that she didn't study psychology at university. (not studying)

'I _____ at university.'

6 When she was a child, Miranda's ambition was to be a vet. (liked to be)

'When I was young, I _____ .'

Preparatory *it*

3 Complete the email by writing one word in each gap.

Hi Ella,

Thank you so much for letting me stay last weekend. It was great (1) _____ you and spending time with your friends. In fact, I had such a good time that it was quite hard (2) _____ leave on Sunday evening!

I really enjoyed our day trip to the caves. I took some great photos and (3) _____ would be nice to share them with you and the others. Shall I email them to you? If not, I could get them printed and send you the prints. (4) _____ so nice to share photos with friends, don't you agree?

I thought Liz and Carlos were lovely, so friendly! But I wasn't sure about Dominic – he didn't seem to enjoy himself very much. Maybe he found our trip to the caves a bit boring. It seems (5) _____ he's the sort of person that prefers the city to the countryside. My brother Dave is exactly the same – (6) _____ impossible to get him to go anywhere!

Next time you must come and stay with me. I've got a sofa bed so it will be easy for you (7) _____ stay. And it will be great fun (8) _____ you here in my flat. I'm dying to show you around the town and there are some great clubs here so you won't get bored. Let's try and arrange it soon!

Lots of love,

Sandy

Memory

4 Choose the correct options.

1 As he gets older, he's getting more and more _____ . It's so sad.

a forget   b forgetful   c forgetting

2 I get really _____ when I look at these old photos.

a nostalgic   b remembering   c nostalgia

3 _____ me, what was the name of your first boyfriend?

a Remember   b Remind   c Reminisce

4 Do you _____ when we used to go to the beach?

a remind   b memory   c remember

5 My grandparents love to _____ about the old days.

a reminisce   b nostalgic   c remind

6 The fantastic atmosphere made the trip really _____ .

a memory   b memorable   c nostalgia

Appearance

5 Replace the words in brackets with a suitable word to complete the sentences.

1 Derek is _____ (he doesn't have a beard) and has dark blond hair.

2 Mrs Arkwright is 85 and her face is covered in _____ (lines).

3 When he was young Jason had a full head of hair but now I'm afraid he's _____ (got no hair on his head).

4 Although her parents have straight hair, Jo's hair is rather _____ (shaped like the letter 'S').

5 My brother started doing body-building a few years ago and now he's very _____ (has lots of muscles).

6 Even when he wears suits, Henry manages to look _____ (untidy).

7 Everyone in my family has _____ (light brown) hair.

8 To be successful in Hollywood you usually have to be _____ (handsome or pretty).

9 I thought Daniela's hair was naturally blonde but in fact it's _____ (artificially coloured).

10 She has a small _____ (shaped like the letter 'O') face and thick dark hair.

Feelings

6 Use the clues to complete the crossword.

Across

2 when you're not sure you believe that something is true

5 the opposite of *pessimistic*

6 when something you were worried about turns out to be OK

7 when you want to find out what's happening and why

9 the way children feel before a holiday or birthday

10 slightly worried, not relaxed

Down

1 the opposite of *interested*

2 when you think somebody is hiding something bad

3 not certain, not sure, not clear

4 angry

8 when you see or hear something you weren't expecting or prepared for

Idioms to describe people

7 Find the mistakes in six of these sentences and correct them.

1 Alison can be very irritating; she's a real pain of the neck.

2 Joe may be a bit boring but his heart is in the right position.

3 He doesn't find it easy to make friends; in fact, he's rather a cold fish.

4 Karen often says things that hurt people but she doesn't care – she's as hard as a nail.

5 Mike is such a know-everything; he always thinks he knows the answer to every question.

6 When I was young I was a bit of a loner; I didn't have many friends.

7 My colleague's not very ambitious and she certainly isn't a high-flying.

8 Kurt can be such an awkward custom, he's always creating problems for us.

How to...

8 Choose the correct words in *italics*.

1 We should take some warm clothes *as/so that* it can be quite cold there at this time of year.

2 We need to apply for the tickets as soon as possible *since/in order to* get the best seats.

3 I used my membership card *because/to* get a discount on the price.

4 I'll take my mobile phone *so that/since* we can stay in touch while I'm away.

5 I didn't invite you *because/so that* there isn't enough space in my car.

Listening

1 **a** 🔵 21 Cover the audioscript. Listen to the dialogue and answer the questions.

1 How many speakers are there?

_____

2 What are they trying to decide?

_____

3 What do they decide to do in the end?

_____

b Listen again and write T (Tom), B (Ben) or A (Alice).

1 fancies eating a burger ☐
2 likes fried chicken ☐
3 suggests going to a pizza place ☐
4 loves pizza ☐
5 is supposed to be on a diet ☐
6 thinks burgers aren't as fattening as pizzas ☐
7 doesn't like vegetarian burgers ☐
8 loves king prawns ☐

c Now look at the audioscript. Write the adjectives and phrases from the box in the correct column.

> greasy   to be sick of something   starving
> delicious   not too keen on   disgusting
> yummy   tasteless   ravenous
> I could eat a horse   scrumptious

Feeling very hungry	Positive opinion	Negative opinion

AUDIOSCRIPT

Tom: I haven't eaten since lunch time and I'm starving. Do either of you feel like popping out for a take-away?

Ben: Great idea, Tom. I'm ravenous.

Alice: Me too. I could eat a horse! Could you get something for me as well?

Tom: (1) <u>What do you fancy</u>?

Alice: Mm. I'm not sure. A burger, I suppose.

Tom: OK. What about you, Ben?

Ben: I'm not too keen on burgers, really. How about fried chicken or something?

Alice: Oh, that's disgusting, so greasy.

Tom: Actually, I was thinking of pizza for myself. There's that new pizza place near the station. It's called Pizza Delight, or something like that. (2) <u>Does that appeal to either of you</u>?

Alice: Yummy. I love pizza.

Ben: Yuk. I'm sick of pizzas. I've had them twice this week already.

Tom: I thought you were on a diet, Ben.

Alice: Yeah. He's on the pizza diet!

Ben: Very funny, Alice. (3) <u>And I suppose burgers are super healthy, are they</u>?

Alice: Well, I'm sure they're not as fattening as pizzas. Anyway, I was going to have a vegetarian burger.

Ben: (4) <u>A vegetarian burger</u>? They're completely tasteless. Like eating cardboard!

Tom: Look. There's no point arguing. We need to agree on something.

Ben: What about kebabs?

Tom: Oh no. I had one of those a couple of days ago and it gave me a bit of a stomach ache.

Alice: I know! (5) <u>What about Chinese</u>?

Ben: Good idea. There's a Chinese take-away in Arnold Street. It's just around the corner from the supermarket. They do that delicious Peking Duck ...

Tom: Yes. And they've got those scrumptious king prawns. Great. Chinese it is!

Pronunciation | intonation: questions

2 **a** Look at the underlined questions (1–5) in the audioscript. Match them with the uses (a or b).

a asking for information we don't know

_____ , _____ , _____

b checking information we already know

_____ , _____

b 🔵 22 Listen and check.

Grammar | quantifiers

3 Choose the correct words to complete the advert.

Riverside Technical College

Student Facilities

Here are just (1) _____ the facilities we provide for our students. We hope you'll agree we have something to offer everyone!

Computer and Internet Centre

You're always connected at Riverside! We have (2) _____ computers available, all with free access to the Internet. There are (3) _____ printers too – so you can print out your essays with ease. And if you need (4) _____ advice, we have two full-time computer technicians available.

Student Café and Bar

(5) _____ students enjoy taking their lunch here. We have a range of delicious snacks, including healthy salads and sandwiches. We're open until midnight, so why not invite (6) _____ friends and spend the evening with us? Or just pop in for (7) _____ coffee and a slice of our homemade cake.

College Sports Centre

Why not improve your health with (8) _____ exercise? Riverside has an extensive range of sports facilities. We have state of the art exercise machines in our gym and a fabulous heated swimming pool. In fact, some of our students spend (9) _____ their free time here. There are (10) _____ colleges in the country which can rival our sports provision, and it's all free for students!

	a		b		c
1	a few		some		a few of
2	much		many		any
3	lots of		any		much
4	an		many		some
5	Few		A lot of		Much
6	a few		a little		few
7	a		a piece of		little
8	many		little		a little
9	a great deal of		many		a lot
10	a few		little		few

4 Tick (✓) the correct sentence in each pair. Sometimes both sentences are correct.

1. a I eat two eggs every morning. ☐
   b She got egg all down the front of her dress. ☐
2. a He bought me some chocolates for my birthday. ☐
   b She's diabetic so she can't eat chocolate. ☐
3. a I need some legal advice. ☐
   b The doctor gave her three advices. ☐
4. a My new car has excellent equipments. ☐
   b Will you bring the camping equipment? ☐
5. a Pedro's knowledge of computers is impressive. ☐
   b Knowledge are very important in the modern world. ☐
6. a I often feel nostalgic for the old times. ☐
   b There never seems to be enough time. ☐

Vocabulary | food and cooking

5 Complete the sentences (1–6) using a word from box A and a word from box B.

A	B
electric	milk
grilled	eggs
grated	cook
scrambled	cheese
sour	cooker
a talented	sausages

1. I love putting _____ _____ on top of pasta.
2. We don't have gas in our area so we had to buy an _____ _____ for the kitchen.
3. We're having a barbeque with _____ _____ and burgers.
4. Would you prefer toast or _____ _____ for breakfast tomorrow?
5. Edwina's husband is a _____ _____ .
6. The smell of _____ _____ is revolting.

How to... | give and check instructions

6 Find the mistakes in six sentences in the dialogue and correct them.

A: I'm going to make a cheese omelette.

B: That sounds delicious. How do you make it?

A: The first, you break two or three eggs into a cup and whisk them up. Grate some cheese and add it to the eggs. Finally, you heat up some butter in a frying pan. You must do sure the butter's nice and hot. Then you pour the egg mix into the pan.

B: So, you mean it you mix the cheese in with the eggs before you put them in the pan?

A: Yes, but you can also add more cheese later.

B: OK.

A: Then you leave the egg and cheese mixture to cook for a few seconds. But you should careful be not to let it get too hot.

B: Is because it can burn?

A: Yes. Exactly.

Reading

1 a Read the article quickly and choose the best title.

1 Impressionist Paintings at Sotheby's
2 The Story of Sotheby's
3 Britain's Greatest Auction House

b Read the article again and match the topics (1–8) with the information (a–h).

1 Sotheby's
2 Samuel Baker
3 James Christie
4 the auction of Talleyrand's library
5 Peter Wilson
6 the first public auction of impressionist masterpieces
7 Parke-Bernet
8 Alfred Taubman

a John Sotheby's rival
b 1958
c chairman of Sotheby's
d the most famous auction house
e an American businessman
f John Sotheby's uncle
g 1793
h a New York auction house

c Match words or phrases in the article with the meanings (1–8).

1 worth a lot _____
2 state an opinion that others disagree with _____
3 competitor _____
4 copy someone's example _____
5 effect/impression/influence _____
6 best/highest quality examples of works of art _____
7 time when the economy is bad _____
8 completely _____

There is little doubt that Sotheby's is the oldest and most famous auction house in the world. It has been going for more than two and a half centuries and has sold many of the most famous and valuable treasures and works of art ever created. Its rivals might disagree but many would argue that the international art market as it exists today (1) _____ (create) by Sotheby's. The idea of enormously valuable works of art being sold at public auction is something we take for granted, but in fact it is a relatively new phenomenon. So how did it all come about?

It all began back in 1744 when a book dealer called Samuel Baker opened a small book store in the Strand in London. After his death in 1778 the business (2) _____ (take over) by his nephew, John Sotheby. Sotheby had a great rival, James Christie, who (3) _____ (start) the Christie's auction house in 1766. Buying and selling things at auction was made fashionable by James Christie but John Sotheby was quick to follow his lead. In 1793 he

auctioned Talleyrand's library and in 1823 he (4) _____ (score) a public relations triumph by auctioning Napoleon's collection of books from St Helena.

Sotheby's business grew throughout the 19th century but it was only in the middle of the 20th century that Sotheby's began to make a huge impact internationally. In 1958 its charismatic chairman, Peter Wilson, (5) _____ (organise) the first ever public auction of impressionist masterpieces by Cezanne, Renoir and Van Gogh. Before that time extremely valuable works such as

these (6) _____ (sell) privately or through dealers. Wilson turned the whole auction into a fashionable event. He sent invitations to film stars and politicians and held the auction in the evening. Journalists from the leading papers (7) _____ (invite) and everyone was asked to wear black tie or evening dress. Not surprisingly, the auction got a huge amount of publicity and the prices set new records.

With its growing reputation in London Sotheby's decided to expand into the American market and bought the New York auction house Parke-Bernet. But things began to go wrong during the oil crisis and the recession of the 1970s and the company started to get into financial difficulties. In 1971 they even tried to raise money by launching a Sotheby's brand of cigarette. Eventually, in 1983 Sotheby's (8) _____ (buy) by American businessman, Alfred Taubman. Based in Detroit, Taubman transformed Sotheby's into a wholly American company. In 2000 the company was the first to offer Internet auctions and expanded into worldwide property sales. It was certainly a long way from the little bookshop in the Strand.

Vocabulary | verb phrases about shopping

2 One word in each sentence is incorrect. Find the word and correct it.

1 It's a good idea to keep the refund when you buy expensive things.

2 If we buy ten of these, can we get a bargain of 10%?

3 Auctions are fun but I do get nervous when people start haggling for something I want.

4 I want to buy a new computer but I can't worth it yet.

5 I love buying things in street markets – it's great fun bidding with the market traders.

6 They're moving house next year so they're not sure if it's afford buying a new sofa.

Grammar | passives

3 Complete the article in exercise 1 using active or passive forms of the verbs in brackets.

4 Rewrite the underlined parts of the website using passive forms.

How things are made

(1) **How does the Mint make coins?**
- Long sheets of metal arrive at the mint.
- (2) Somebody feeds the metal strips into a cutting machine.
- (3) The cutting machine cuts the metal into round shapes called 'blanks'.
- (4) After the machine has cut them out somebody heats the blanks in a furnace.
- (5) Somebody washes the blanks while somebody is heating them.
- The hot blanks go into a pressing machine and (6) the machine stamps each coin with a pattern on both sides.
- (7) Somebody cools the coins and a special machine counts them.
- (8) Somebody distributes the coins to the banks.

1 *How are coins made?*

2 _____

3 _____

4 _____

5 _____

6 _____

7 _____

8 _____

5 Write passive sentences using the words given.

1 The doctor has given Alison a new prescription.
Alison *has been given a new prescription.*

2 You mustn't open the present until your birthday.
The present _____

3 The police are investigating the crime.
The crime _____

4 They are going to open the hotel in November.
The hotel _____

5 We will drive the children to the party.
The children _____

6 You can see my house from the top of the hill.
My house _____

7 Someone was watching them.
They _____

8 They haven't released that DVD yet.
That DVD _____

9 Someone might have seen the burglar.
The burglar _____

10 They didn't take anything.
Nothing _____

How to... | complain about goods and services

6 a Choose the correct words in *italics*.

A: Is that customer services?

B: Yes. How can I help you?

A: Well, I'm calling to complain (a) *for/about* my Internet service.

B: What seems to be the problem?

A: It's the wireless signal. It doesn't seem to work properly...

B: I'm terribly (b) *sorry/apologising* about that. Did we supply you with the Internet router?

A: Yes, I'm renting the whole package from you. I think the router's (c) *at fault/faulty*.

B: I can only (d) *give/offer* my apologies for that.

A: But what are you going to do about it?

B: We could send you a (e) *replacement/refund* router.

A: Thank you. And I'd be (f) *grateful/satisfied* if you could send it as soon as possible. I really need to have a reliable Internet connection.

B: Of course. I'll put you on our urgent list and I can (g) *offer/promise* you it'll be sent out tomorrow. Once again, I (h) *can/do* apologise for any inconvenience. We always try to keep our customers satisfied.

b 🔘 23 Listen and check.

Pronunciation | stress: emphasis (2)

7 a Look at the underlined sentences in exercise 6. Which word is stressed in each sentence?

b 🔘 24 Listen and check your answers. Then repeat the sentences.

Listening

1 **a** 🔵 25 Cover the audioscript. Listen to five people talking about animals. Match each person with an animal from the box. Three animals are not needed.

> snake   cats   spider   tropical fish   mouse
> horse   goldfish   dog

1 _____   3 _____   5 _____
2 _____   4 _____

b Listen again and match the statements (1–8) with an animal from exercise 1a.

1 is always hungry _____
2 lives in a big field _____
3 need a lot of care and attention _____
4 loves going for walks _____
5 doesn't jump any more _____
6 provide companionship _____
7 moves very slowly _____
8 costs a lot of money to maintain _____

c Now read the audioscript. Write the words from the box in the table.

> dart   crawl   tank   sinuous   gentle
> kennel   trot   playful   stable

Ways animals move (verbs)	Places animals live (nouns)	Characteristics (adjectives)

AUDIOSCRIPT

1

Well, I'm not sure you'd call them pets, really. I mean you don't have to take them to the vet, or for walks, obviously. But they do require quite a lot of care and attention. I seem to spend ages cleaning out the pond and repairing the water filters. It's a nightmare in autumn with all the fallen leaves. And in winter you have to make sure the surface doesn't get covered in ice. But they do give me a lot of pleasure, watching them darting around.

2

We've had him for about four years now. Er, he's got a kennel in the back garden. His name's Wolfie. David bought him for the children, really. Everyone knows retrievers are great with kids – so gentle and playful. He's got beautiful blond fur and he loves being cuddled. Of course, he adores being taken for walks – which is a great excuse for us to get some exercise as well! The only downside is the amount of food he eats. And whatever we give him, he always seems to be starving.

3

Some people think keeping a reptile is a bit weird, but you'd be surprised at how popular it is. I know loads of people that do it. I got Sarah from a friend and I wasn't too sure about it at first. It's a bit of a fuss because you have to have a big tank and keep it at a certain temperature. And when she sheds her skin it's a bit disgusting. But I think she's beautiful – the way she moves is so slow and sinuous. I love letting her crawl up my arms and around my neck.

4

When I was younger I used to take her out jumping and things, but I hurt my back a few years ago, so now we just go for walks. Or a bit of a gentle trot if I'm feeling energetic! We've got a big field behind the house so she's got plenty of room, and there's a small stable for the winter months. Big animals are always quite expensive to look after, but I think it's worth it. I mean I get plenty of exercise, and I feel we have a really strong bond. I certainly wouldn't let anyone else ride her.

5

I never had any children, but I think in some ways they're better than children. A lot less trouble! I've got two at the moment, Tiddles and Spark. Tiddles is just a kitten, really. Now that I'm retired I don't really get out much, so they're ideal for me, and they're much easier to look after than dogs. They're pretty independent but they give me a lot of companionship. I talk to them all the time, which is a bit stupid I know, but at least I don't get lonely.

Grammar | *have/get something done*

2 Complete the picture labels using forms of *have/ get something done*. Use nouns from box A and verbs from box B.

A	B
car blood pressure house boiler hair eyes	check paint do test service wash

1 Mrs Alderson _____ every month.
2 Daniel _____ once a week.
3 The Smiths _____ every five years.
4 Liz _____ once every six months.
5 Mr Grant _____ when he goes to the clinic.
6 We _____ before the beginning of winter.

3 Rewrite the sentences using the words in brackets.

He needs to finish that project soon. (done)
He needs to get that project done soon.

1 Someone left the bag behind. (got)
_____

2 The maid washes Linda's clothes. (has)
_____

3 They forward my post to me. (I)
_____

4 Will somebody cut your hair this week? (get)
_____

5 How often do they clean your windows? (you)
_____

6 I should finish my homework by six o'clock. (done)
_____

Vocabulary | excess

4 Use the clues to complete the crossword.

1 Everything in that shop is _____ . Let's try somewhere cheaper.
2 It's fun to do something _____ on your birthday.
3 I live in a very remote place so for me a car is a _____ .
4 I have the ultimate _____ – a waterproof TV in my bathroom!
5 Do you think owning 50 pairs of shoes is _____?
5 Karl's rather greedy, he always asks for _____ -large portions.
6 I love _____ food but I can't usually afford it.
7 You don't have to pay, I'll _____ you.
8 Once a month I _____ myself by going out for a good meal at a smart restaurant.
9 Our wealthy neighbours are famous for their _____ entertaining.
10 Tomasz is so _____ – he always expects to get his own way.
11 They say that one day everybody will live to be 200 but that sounds rather far-_____ to me.
12 After she got her pay rise Lucy went on a crazy spending _____ .
13 I'm quite strict. I don't _____ my children.
14 Five foreign holidays a year! Don't you think that's a little over-the-_____ ?
15 Lizzie and Sue _____ themselves by going to the beauty salon once a week.

Passives

1 You have just booked a holiday on the Internet. Read the webpage and complete the sentences (1–10). Use appropriate passive forms.

Thank you
for making a booking with **GoAway Travel**

Your booking reference is HJ980L

We have debited €450 from your credit card. For your security we use 128 KB protection software for all credit card payments.
We are sending your itinerary by email. Remember GoAway Travel is a ticketless airline and we will therefore not be sending you tickets by post.

- You must bring your booking reference number and passport to check-in one hour before departure.
- You cannot change the date and time of your flights.
- You can pre-book seats on the website.
- GoAway Travel does not allow smoking on any of its flights.
- You may purchase meals on the plane.
- The price includes transfers from the airport.

Please see our FAQs if you have any further queries.

1 €450 _____
2 128 KB protection software _____
_____
3 Your itinerary _____
4 Tickets _____
5 Your passport _____
6 The date and time of your flights _____
_____
7 Seats _____
8 Smoking _____
9 Meals _____
10 Transfers from the airport _____
_____

Quantifiers

2 Find the mistakes in eight of these sentences and correct them.

1 Our shop stocks luggages from all over the world.
2 There are few places as beautiful as Kashmir.
3 There isn't many traffic around here on Sundays.
4 May I have little sugar in my coffee, please?
5 I'd like to have a lots of money.
6 I'm not busy, I only have a few work this week.
7 They don't have much money but they're happy.
8 Would you like a spaghetti, or do you prefer rice?
9 You can invite few of your friends if you like.
10 The college offers much IT courses.

have/get something done

3 Complete each sentence with one word.

1 I _____ the central heating checked last month so it should be fine now.
2 She never received her new credit card – it must have _____ lost in the post.
3 I'm sorry about spilling wine on your jacket. I'll have it _____ for you.
4 Tell the boss that Jamie will _____ the report finished by four o'clock.
5 Have you got the broken chair _____ ?
6 He _____ arrested at an anti-pollution demonstration.
7 I like to have my hair _____ by Silvia. She's the best stylist in the salon.
8 I'm going to get my photo _____ I need it for the job application.

How to...

4 Match the sentence beginnings (1–8) with the sentence endings (a–h).

1 I do apologise ☐
2 The important ☐
3 So it sounds ☐
4 My new camcorder seems ☐
5 I'd be grateful ☐
6 You must make ☐
7 Is that because ☐
8 I'm calling ☐

a to be faulty.
b for any inconvenience.
c to complain about your delivery service.
d sure it's not too hot.
e thing is not to burn the milk.
f there are several different answers?
g if you could give me a refund.
h like there could be quite a few problems?

Food and cooking

5 Use the clues to complete the crossword.

1 They say _____ are very good for you.

2 You haven't cooked this, it's completely _____ .

3 Coffee without sugar has this taste.

4 Heat the milk in a small _____ .

5 You have to _____ the mixture quickly until it becomes stiff.

6 Do you prefer to _____ eggs or fry them?

7 I don't eat meat. I'm a _____ .

8 Don't cook my steak for long, I like it _____ .

9 It's delicious. Can you give me the _____ ?

10 I like to _____ a little cheese on top of my pasta.

11 Would you like a _____ of cake?

12 The soup isn't _____ enough, add more.

13 This vegetable contains a lot of vitamins.

14 It's a fruit which we often serve with cream.

15 I don't put sugar in tea or coffee – I hate _____ drinks.

Excess

6 Complete the sentences using words from the box. Two words are not needed.

> spending   excessive   extra-large   far-fetched
> overpriced   spoilt   luxury   extravagant

1 My car isn't a _____ . It's a necessity.

2 You're renting a five-star hotel for your wedding? How _____ !

3 Some people say there is life on Mars but the idea seems _____ to me.

4 After we moved we went on a _____ spree and bought lots of new furniture.

5 Don't buy anything from that shop – all their goods are completely _____ .

6 I think it's greedy to order _____ portions in restaurants.

Verb phrases about shopping

7 Complete the sentences using words from the box.

> afford   bargain   bidding   discount
> haggling   worth   receipt   refund

1 I only paid €5 for this DVD – I got a _____ !

2 I'd love to get a new car but I'm not sure I can _____ it.

3 We love visiting the local markets and _____ for things.

4 I'm afraid you cannot return the goods if you do not have a _____ .

5 Don't interrupt him; he's _____ for something on an Internet auction site.

6 We are offering a 20% _____ to any customers who buy more than five CDs.

7 It's a really expensive trip but we think it's _____ it.

8 Due to the cancellation of tonight's performance we are offering a full _____ to all ticket holders.

Prefixes

8 Choose the correct words in *italics*.

1 It doesn't take long to prepare, just *rewarm/reheat* it in the microwave.

2 He's got a fantastic job with a huge *multinational/manynational* company.

3 Can I have the *ex-large/extra-large* burger, please?

4 We thought the seats on the plane were very *uncomfortable/incomfortable*.

5 Sue's *bilanguaged/bilingual*; she speaks English and German equally well.

6 The children get very badly behaved when they're *extra-tired/overtired*.

7 Have you seen your *ex-boyfriend/exboyfriend* recently?

8 The film was *monotonous/monologue* and quite boring.

9 That chicken was *less-cooked/undercooked* – it was pink in the middle.

10 I've just bought a *multipurpose/monopurpose* printer. It can print, scan and photocopy.

Reading

1 **a** Read the text quickly and choose the best summary for each paragraph. Two summaries are not needed.

a The Fight for Freedom
b Independence
c Studying in London
d Introduction
e Gandhi's Legacy
f Gandhi's Early Life
g Life in Prison
h Philosophy

b Read the text again. Write true (T) or false (F).

1 Gandhi was president of India. ☐
2 Gandhi worked in South Africa. ☐
3 South Africa used to be part of the British empire. ☐
4 Local people were sometimes treated badly in the colonies. ☐
5 The British were never able to put Gandhi in prison. ☐
6 Some elements of Satyagraha come from Hinduism. ☐
7 Gandhi wanted India to be mainly Hindu. ☐
8 A religious extremist killed Gandhi. ☐

c Write notes to complete this time-line of Gandhi's life.

1869	born in Porbandar ...
1893	
1915	
1947	
1948	

Leading by example

(1) Gandhi is one of history's great leaders. But unlike other leaders he never led an army, he was never a president or prime minister and he never used force or violence to impose his leadership on people. His principle of leadership was simple – he led by example. He believed that the best way to influence events was through peaceful protest rather than by violent revolution or bloodshed.

(2) Mohandas Karamchand Gandhi was born on 2nd October 1869 in Porbandar in western India. He was sent to England to study law and was offered a job in South Africa after he qualified in 1893. At that time both India and South Africa were colonies of Britain. Working as a lawyer, Gandhi soon began to experience the prejudice that local people suffered under the colonial regime.

(3) Gandhi returned to India in 1915, determined to fight against colonialism and injustice. He realised that Indians would never be able to build a fair society until they had independence from the British empire. He joined the Indian nationalist movement and began to fight for Indian independence. The British regarded Gandhi as a troublemaker and he was arrested many times. Rather than resist, Gandhi was quite prepared to be sent to prison for his beliefs. Altogether he spent more than seven years behind bars.

(4) Most independence movements in history have depended on violence and revolution to achieve their aims. Gandhi was sure that the same effect could be achieved through non-violent protest and a policy of civil disobedience. He developed a philosophy known as 'Satyagraha' which was partly based on the teachings of Hinduism. According to Satyagraha the best way to change society was through peaceful means. Through his own behaviour Gandhi provided an example of this philosophy in action.

(5) After more than 30 years of struggle India eventually achieved independence in 1947. Gandhi's policy of peaceful protests, strikes, trade boycotts and civil disobedience had worked. Gandhi wanted India to be a single country which included all races and religions but his wish was not granted. The Indian sub-continent was split into two states – the mainly Hindu India and the largely Muslim Pakistan.

(6) Gandhi's belief in religious freedom was to cost him his life. On 30th January 1948 he was assassinated by a young Hindu fanatic, Nathuram Godse. But his legacy was to last long after his death. Gandhi's philosophy of peaceful protest and civil disobedience has been an inspiration to numerous people around the world. By his own actions he showed that the best leaders are those who lead by example rather than by force.

Grammar | *It's time/I'd rather/I'd better*

2 Tick (✓) the sentence (a or b) which has the same meaning as the original sentence.

1 It's time you went to bed.
   a You should be in bed by now. ☐
   b You are already in bed. ☐

2 I'd rather take the bus.
   a There is no other way to get there. ☐
   b I prefer buses to trains. ☐

3 We'd better take the earlier flight.
   a We prefer early flights. ☐
   b The later flight might not arrive in time. ☐

4 Would you rather I replied by email?
   a I prefer to send emails. ☐
   b Do you want me to send an email? ☐

5 It's time you looked for a job.
   a You've been looking but you haven't found the perfect job yet. ☐
   b You are unemployed. ☐

6 I'd rather she didn't come.
   a I don't want her to come. ☐
   b She doesn't want to come. ☐

7 You'd better take the car.
   a There's a bus strike today. ☐
   b You prefer driving. ☐

8 It's time we left.
   a It's quite late. ☐
   b We left on time. ☐

3 Rewrite the sentences using the words in brackets.

1 I really think you should move to a bigger flat. (time)
   _____

2 You should take an umbrella. (better)
   _____

3 I prefer going to the cinema. (rather)
   _____

4 John needs to get a better computer. (it's)
   _____

5 Do you want me to bring my camera? (would)
   _____

6 I would prefer her not to smoke. (didn't)
   _____

7 I don't like working at the weekend. (rather)
   _____

8 I think it's safer if you have the salad. (you'd)
   _____

Vocabulary | describing personality

4 Use the clues to complete the crossword.

1 My girlfriend tricks people into doing what she wants. She's very _____ .

2 She's quite _____ , so she doesn't enjoy meeting new people.

3 I've got strong ideas about everything; I suppose I'm pretty _____ .

4 When complaining you should be firm but not _____ .

5 Lizzie never makes a fuss or complains. She's very _____-going.

6 Karl only thinks about himself and ignores other people's wishes, he's very _____ .

7 My sister's very _____ – if she wants to do something, no one can stop her!

8 He doesn't have any secrets. He's very _____ and honest.

9 I wish I could be more _____ but I tend to let other people take the lead.

10 We always laugh when Jake tells a story because he's so _____ .

11 My boss is very single-_____ . He never gets distracted.

How to... | introduce general and specific points

5 Choose the correct words in *italics*.

(1) *General/Generally*, I'm a fairly calm person. As a (2) *rule/regulation*, I don't feel nervous in work or social situations and most of (3) *times/the time* I'm relaxed and happy. But everything changes when I have to get on a plane, (4) *special/especially* if it's a long flight. (5) *Suddenly/Sudden*, I change into a nervous wreck! I sweat and I can't concentrate. I (6) *actually feel/feel actually* sure that something bad's going to happen – it's awful!

Listening

1 **a** 🔘 26 Cover the audioscript. Listen and answer the questions.

1 Where are the two people?

_____

2 What is Amanda's job?

_____

3 What are Steven's aims?

_____

b Listen again and complete each sentence with one word.

1 Steven has been training for _____ weeks.

2 He hasn't done any real exercise for _____ years.

3 Steven thinks three months is an _____ long time.

4 He is _____ eating desserts.

5 He _____ hungry all the time.

6 Amanda asks Steven about his _____ levels.

7 Steven used to feel _____ in the afternoons.

8 Amanda hasn't prepared the _____ sheet for Steven yet.

c Find the expressions from the box in the audioscript. Use them to complete the sentences (1–6).

> get fit   be positive   catching up   cut out
> feeling lethargic   slave driver

1 A strong cup of coffee often helps if you are

_____ .

2 My boss is a real _____ – she makes me work hard all day.

3 After Alice's operation it took her several months to _____ again.

4 Zoe missed two months of school so she's got a lot of _____ to do.

5 I try to _____ but sometimes life makes me quite depressed.

6 If you _____ bread and cakes, you'll soon start to lose weight.

AUDIOSCRIPT

Amanda: Come on Steven, keep going!

Steven: This is exhausting …

Amanda: One more repetition. You can do it … Great. Well done! Let's take a short break now.

Steven: Phew! Good idea!

Amanda: You're doing really well, you know.

Steven: I'm still finding it quite difficult.

Amanda: Well, you can't expect to get completely fit in just a month.

Steven: Actually, it's been six weeks.

Amanda: Six weeks then. You know it usually takes about three months to get fit. After all, you haven't done any real exercise for more than five years, so you've got some catching up to do.

Steven: Mm. It seems an awfully long time.

Amanda: Be positive. We're almost halfway there.

Steven: How long before I start to lose weight?

Amanda: That depends. Have you cut out all those sweet snacks?

Steven: Er, sort of. But I'm afraid I'm still eating desserts. I just feel so hungry all the time.

Amanda: How about trying fruit instead of a dessert?

Steven: OK. I'll give it a try.

Amanda: If you cut down the amount of sugar you eat, you're bound to lose weight. Now, how about your energy levels? Are you still feeling lethargic in the afternoons?

Steven: No, that's definitely improved. I haven't really felt as tired as I used to.

Amanda: That's great.

Steven: Oh, have you prepared that nutrition sheet for me?

Amanda: Sorry. I'm afraid I forgot. I'll do it next week. So, are you ready to move on to the next machine?

Steven: Gosh. You trainers are such slave drivers!

Vocabulary | adjectives and intensifiers

2 Complete the sentences using intensifiers. Use *absolutely* with non-gradable adjectives and *very* with gradable adjectives.

1 Saturday's game is _____ vital for our hopes of promotion.

2 I always feel _____ hungry after swimming.

3 I often feel _____ tired at the end of the day.

4 Terry was _____ devastated when the factory closed down.

5 Suzanne was _____ exhausted after the race.

6 Poor Joe! He's _____ upset about his exam results.

7 What's there to eat? I'm _____ starving!

8 Take your time to decide. This is a _____ important decision for you.

Grammar | reported speech

3 🔘 27 Cover the audioscript. Listen to five examples of direct speech from the dialogue. Write them in reported speech using the words given.

1 Steven said _____ _____

2 Amanda told Steven _____ _____

3 Amanda asked Steven _____ _____

4 Steven said _____ _____

5 Steven asked Amanda _____ _____

4 Match each example of reported speech (1–8) with the quoted direct speech (a–h).

1 He said he'd been out for a meal. ☐
2 He said he was going out for a meal. ☐
3 He said he'd never been out for meals. ☐
4 He said he never goes out for meals. ☐
5 He said he went out for a meal the day before. ☐
6 He said he would go out for a meal that day. ☐
7 He asked if she was going out for a meal. ☐
8 He asked if she'd been out for a meal. ☐

a He said, 'I've never been out for meals.'

b He said, 'I went out for a meal yesterday.'

c He said, 'I've been out for a meal.'

d He asked, 'Have you been out for a meal?'

e He asked, 'Are you going out for a meal?'

f He said, 'I'm going out for a meal.'

g He said, 'I'll go out for a meal today.'

h He said, 'I never go out for meals.'

5 Choose the correct words to complete the sentences.

1 When we were young our parents ____ not to talk to strangers.
   a told   b told to us
   c told us

2 James asked me what ____ for my birthday.
   a I wanted   b did I want
   c wanted me

3 My girlfriend asked me ____ go to the party with her.
   a will I   b if I would
   c that I would

4 He said ____ already bought the tickets.
   a me he had   b he had
   c to me he had

5 The doctor ____ that I should lose some weight.
   a said me   b told to me
   c said

6 Davina asked me ____ been the day before.
   a where I   b where I had
   c where was I

7 The guard told ____ photos in the museum.
   a us not to take b not to take
   c that not to take

8 Michael asked us ____ the film last Wednesday.
   a did we enjoy   b if we had enjoyed
   c if we enjoy

9 She asked me whether ____ a school uniform when I was at infant school.
   a I must wear   b I had to wear
   c did I have to wear

10 She asked me how much ____ for it.
   a did I pay   b have I paid
   c I paid

Pronunciation | intonation: reporting

6 **a** Look again at the sentences in exercise 4. Do we use a higher intonation for reported speech or direct speech?

Higher intonation: _____

Lower intonation: _____

b 🔘 28 Listen and repeat the sentences.

Reading

1 **a** Read the article and match the sentence halves.

1 Piers Sharma ☐
2 Mike Ryde ☐
3 Arran Fernandez ☐
4 Francesca ☐
5 Frederick ☐

a took a Maths exam at the age of five.

b is a college principal.

c is taking a school leaving exam next year.

d is six years old.

e is waiting for his exam results.

b Find the mistake in each sentence and correct them.

1 Exam results are coming out later this month.

2 Piers Sharma got an A* in the exam.

3 There are five students in Piers' class at school.

4 The college has a maths course for babies.

5 Mike Ryde's son is top of the class at school.

6 The parents decide when children are ready to take an exam.

7 Mike says the older children love working with computers.

8 Mike thinks few children could take a school leaving exam at the age of 11.

c Match words and phrases from the article (1–10) with the meanings (a–j).

1 trepidation ☐
2 momentarily ☐
3 extraordinarily ☐
4 embarked ☐
5 coincidence ☐
6 knock-on effect ☐
7 gravitate ☐
8 horrified ☐
9 dumb down ☐
10 lowest common denominator ☐

a when two things are the same for no reason

b surprisingly

c lower the standard

d causes other things to happen

e slight nervousness or fear

f shocked, frightened

g least difficult thing that everyone understands

h for a very short period of time

i attracted towards

j began

Who's a clever boy then?

Is it wise for children aged six and seven to be taking school leaving exams?

Like many youngsters across the country, Piers Sharma will be waiting for the postman with trepidation next month, when exam results come out. Being seven years old, he is not the average examination student, however.

'It was a bit hard, and a bit easy,' he says of the exam in computer skills. 'The hard bit was the video conferencing, the applications bit was easy.'

Does he expect to pass? Sharma sounds momentarily stressed. 'I did really well in the practical, I got an A*,' he says. 'In the exam, I might have got a C+ or a B+.'

Most students do their school leaving exams at the age of 15 or 16, but Sharma is one of a growing number of pupils sitting exams extraordinarily early. This year, he is one of an entire class of nine children – four seven-year-olds and five six-year-olds – who in May took an exam in information and communication technology (ICT) at the private Ryde College in Hertfordshire.

The course takes a year to complete. Mike Ryde, principal of the college, confirmed that three of the children were five years old when they embarked on their examination studies, having 'graduated' from the college's baby and toddler computer course, where learning starts at 18 months. At the age of three or four the infants attend 'primer' lessons. Then Ryde judges when they are ready to sit the exam.

'The most we've ever had before has been one or two children of this age doing a school leaving exam,' says Ryde. 'The very fact that we've got nine students this year shows that a lot of six and seven-year-olds would be capable of doing this. It is no coincidence that they all started in classes so early.'

The youngest ever to have taken the exam at Ryde was Arran Fernandez, who was five when he took Maths in 2001. Ryde's own daughter Francesca, seven, will take the ICT examination next year and his son Frederick, six, is on the primer course. 'The wonderful thing is that studying at a level designed for a 15-year-old has a knock-on effect,' he says. 'Francesca is topping the class at school.'

'We also have children doing English and Maths really early, but the younger children seem to gravitate towards ICT,' he says. 'They love working with computers.'

Many educationists and parents would be horrified, arguing that six is too young to burden a child with exams. Ryde, however, believes that early school leaving exams should be introduced widely, claiming that such a system would reduce the stress on youngsters later on.

'At present, you see children taking upwards of ten examinations at once at the age of 16,' he says. 'That's a tremendous pressure. Why not give them the opportunity to take one or two a year? It seems to me that most children are ready to do an examination by the age of 11. We should not dumb down the system to the lowest common denominator – education is all about opportunity.'

How to ... | report the results of a survey

2 Choose the correct words in *italics*.

Thank you for returning all the surveys to us. We have now checked through your responses and here are the collated results.

For question 1, 25 (1) *from/out of* 30 said that they watched TV for more than two hours a day. The (2) *vast/big* majority said they mainly watched soap operas and talent shows. Only 20% (3) *of/out* the group watched news and current affairs programmes.

For question 2, (4) *all people/everyone* admitted using a mobile phone at least once a day. (5) *Nearly/Quite* half the group used their phones ten or more times a day. (6) *Most/Majority* people used their phones for texting.

For question 3 we had some very interesting responses. A (7) *vast/small* minority bought their music on CDs, but the (8) *majority/most* of people downloaded music from the Internet. (9) *Not any people/No one* thought it was wrong to share MP3 music files.

Grammar | reporting verbs

3 Match the sentence halves.

1 The mechanic <u>suggested</u> ☐
2 When questioned by the police, the thief <u>denied</u> ☐
3 Before the trip, Caroline <u>reminded</u> ☐
4 In court, the lawyer <u>claimed</u> ☐
5 The dentist <u>warned</u> ☐
6 The TV advertisement <u>claimed</u> ☐

a taking money from the woman's purse.
b that the prisoner had taken money from the woman's purse.
c that their washing powder was the best one on the market.
d me not to eat so many sweets in future.
e selling the car and buying a more reliable model.
f us to bring our tickets and ID cards with us.

4 Report these examples of direct speech (1–6) using reporting verbs from the box.

admit   confirm   deny   explain   ~~remind~~
suggest   warn

David [Don't forget to lock the back door.]

David reminded me to lock the back door.

1 **My brother** [Why don't we go out for a meal?]

_____

2 **John** [I can't come because I have to work that evening.]

_____

3 **The children** [We didn't take it.]

_____

4 **The lifeguard** [Swimming after eating can be very dangerous.]

_____

5 **Maria** [The reason I failed the exam was because I never did my homework.]

_____

6 **The sales representative** [Yes, we can deliver the parcel tomorrow.]

_____

It's time/I'd rather/I'd better

1 Write one word in each gap.

1 It's getting late. I think it's _____ we left.
2 Would you _____ take the bus or the train?
3 Your bedroom's filthy. _____ time you tidied up.
4 Look at those dark clouds, you'd _____ take an umbrella.
5 I'm a bit tired. I _____ rather not go out this evening.
6 Don't you think it's time you _____ your mother? You can use my mobile.
7 She's looking very ill. You _____ better call a doctor.
8 _____ you rather pay me now or wait until next week?
9 You'd better _____ interrupt him right now, he's with a client.
10 I'd rather _____ poor and happy than rich and unhappy.

Reported speech

2 Steve got an answer-phone message a few days ago. Read the message and report the underlined information.

Hi Steve, it's Danielle. (0) I'm sorry you're not there. (1) I tried your mobile but there was no reply. (2) Are you out playing football today? Listen, (3) I'm phoning because I need some advice. The thing is, (4) my landlord has asked me to leave the flat. (5) He wants me to go at the end of this month. Obviously, (6) I'm very worried about it. I know you know a lot about the law, (7) can you give me any advice? Please call me back later, (8) I'll be at home all day tomorrow. Thanks.

0 Danielle said *she was sorry that he wasn't there.*
1 She said _____
2 She asked _____
3 She said _____
4 She told _____
5 She said _____
6 She said _____
7 She asked _____
8 She told _____

Reporting verbs

3 Match the examples of direct speech (a–j) with the reported speech sentences (1–10). Then complete the sentences.

a Don't touch these plates, they're very hot. ☐
b Where's your passport? ☐
c I'm afraid the doctor's sick today so he can't see you. ☐
d Don't forget to be at the airport two hours before your departure. ☐
e Do all the exercises on page 65 of the Workbook. ☐
f You'll have to get a new hard drive for your laptop. ☐
g Are you feeling alright, darling? ☐
h Why don't we go to the cinema on Friday evening? ☐
i I stole the money. ☐
j We didn't copy our homework from the Internet. ☐

1 The receptionist explained _____
2 Our teacher told us _____
3 My best friend suggested _____
4 The waitress warned us _____
5 The criminal admitted he _____
6 The immigration officer asked me _____
7 My mother asked me _____
8 The computer engineer confirmed _____
9 The travel agent reminded us _____
10 The children denied _____

Success

4 Match the sentence halves.

1 Clara considered bringing up three healthy children to be her greatest ☐
2 Shane's very irritating – he's always showing off and ☐
3 It was a challenging task but in the end we ☐
4 When I think of everything our company has achieved it's hard not to ☐
5 People say that in this life you need a lot of luck in order to ☐
6 We've never done this before but we're willing to ☐
7 After failing the driving test four times, Jim has decided to ☐
8 She was so successful at school that we knew Ana would be a ☐

a be proud.
b achievement.
c succeed.
d boasting.
e high-achiever.
f managed it.
g have a go.
h give up.

Describing personality

5 Choose the correct words in *italics*.

1 My cousin can be very *single-minded/aggressive*. Once he's made up his mind, nothing can stop him!
2 I'm pretty *headstrong/proactive* – I don't take any notice of what other people think.
3 Isabel loves parties. She's very *outgoing/easy-going*.
4 My boss can be very *opinionated/manipulative* so I don't really trust him.
5 You must invite Carol to the party – she's very *single-minded/witty* and she'll make us all laugh.
6 It takes a long time for David to relax in social situations, as he's very *outgoing/introverted*.
7 We're looking for a new marketing manager who will be *proactive/open* in developing the business.
8 Too many sugary drinks make him *headstrong/aggressive* and he starts fighting the other children.
9 Don't be so *selfish/single-minded*; leave some of the chocolate for us.
10 She never listens to reasonable arguments. She's very *opinionated/single-minded*.

Adjectives/intensifiers

6 In six sentences the underlined adjective is incorrect. Find the mistakes and correct them.

1 I was very <u>devastated</u> when I heard the news.
2 She loves cleaning. Her kitchen is very <u>spotless</u>.
3 My flat is nice but it's absolutely <u>small</u>.
4 I'm really <u>hungry</u>. What's in the fridge?
5 The guided tour was absolutely <u>interesting</u>.
6 It's absolutely <u>vital</u> that you take out insurance.
7 Robert was very <u>ecstatic</u> about his pay rise.
8 New York can be absolutely <u>cold</u> in January.

Phrasal verbs with three parts

7 Complete each gap with a word from the box.

> catch   come   cut   for   get   look   looking
> made   on   put   to (x2)   with (x4)

1 He's my hero. I really _____ up _____ him.
2 If you want to lose weight, you'll have to _____ down _____ all those sweets and cakes!
3 I hear you've got a new car. I'm _____ forward _____ seeing it.
4 Joe's snoring is very irritating – I don't know how you _____ up _____ it.
5 Carol has _____ up _____ a great new idea to make money.
6 They've caught the bank robbers. I'm glad they didn't _____ away _____ it.
7 The runner was slow at first but she _____ up _____ it in the last few metres and won.
8 He's just gone to the shops. You can _____ up _____ him if you run.

How to...

8 Complete the sentences with words and phrases from the box. Two are not needed.

> a rule   minority   nearly   nobody
> on the whole   out of   suddenly   vast

1 Forty-five _____ 50 people said that they watched TV for more than two hours a day.
2 _____ , I enjoy meeting new people.
3 The _____ majority used their computers for doing homework.
4 As _____ , I tend to avoid aggressive people.
5 A small _____ of people claimed they didn't even own a mobile phone.
6 Social networking sites were used by _____ half the group.

Vocabulary | law and insurance

1 **a** Each sentence contains one word which should be in a different sentence. Find the words and put them in the correct sentences.

1 The judge convicted the man to three years in prison.
2 There was a fire at the factory last week; the police think it is fraud.
3 I fell down the steps at work so I sentenced the company and got compensation.
4 You shouldn't use someone else's credit card, that's premium.
5 I'm glad to say I've never been sued of any driving offences.
6 If you insure fraud, you are sure to be found out eventually.
7 The arson on our house insurance seems to get higher every year.
8 You should always commit your house against fire and burglary.

b Complete the sentences with one word.

1 I was shocked when my next-door neighbour was convicted _____ fraud.
2 The injured pedestrian sued the driver _____ €10,000.
3 The convicted man was sentenced _____ five years in prison.
4 The over-confident criminal believed he would get away _____ the crime.

Reading

2 **a** Read the website on page 69 quickly and match the headings (a–f) with the stories (1–3). Three headings are not needed.

a **Fatal Coffee**

b **The Unlucky Car Thief**

c **Imprisoned in a Garage**

d **Nightclub Accident**

e **Don't Ask the Jury**

f **Cruise Control**

b Read the website again and write questions for the answers below.

1 It maintains the vehicle's speed.
_____
_____

2 To make himself a cup of coffee.
_____
_____

3 A broken arm and leg and cuts to the head.
_____
_____

4 To avoid paying the entrance charge.
_____
_____

5 $12,000
_____
_____

6 For ten years.
_____
_____

7 Because the owners were on vacation.
_____
_____

8 A supply of dog food and some cans of Pepsi.
_____
_____

c Find the words and phrases from the box in the website and write them in the correct column.

> accelerator awarded broke compensation
> court cruise control expenses fell jury
> knocked out mph owner's manual speed
> starvation suffered

Vehicles	Injuries/Harm	Legal

Compensation Culture or Legal Legends?

1 _____

A few years ago, Joseph Grazinski bought a brand-new motor home. He was thrilled because it had cruise control – a switch on the steering wheel which controls the accelerator and maintains the vehicle's speed at a constant rate. A few days after buying the motor home he decided to take it on a trip to Yellowstone National Park. Having joined the motorway, he set the cruise control at 65 mph and decided to step into the back of the motor home to make himself a cup of coffee. Within seconds the motor home had veered off the road, slid down a hillside and turned upside down. Mr Grazinski broke an arm and a leg and suffered cuts to his head.

Mr Grazinski sued the manufacturers because it did not say in the owner's manual that it was dangerous to leave the steering wheel while driving, even if the cruise control was switched on. The court awarded him $175,000 and a brand-new motor home.

2 _____

Kara Walton of Claymont, Delaware wanted to get into the Black Cat nightclub but she didn't want to pay the $3.50 entrance charge. So she decided to sneak into the club by climbing through the window of the ladies toilet. Unfortunately, while struggling to get through the window, she fell to the floor and knocked out her two front teeth.

Ms Walton sued the owner of the Black Cat nightclub and was awarded $12,000 compensation plus dental expenses.

3 _____

For ten years Terrence Dickson of Bristol, Pennsylvania, had had a successful career as a burglar who specialised in robbing people's houses while they were on holiday. He was about to leave a house he had just robbed when he got stuck in the garage. After entering the garage from the house, he realised the door could not be opened from the inside. Because the owners were on vacation he was trapped in the garage for another eight days. During this time he lived on the supply of dog food and some cans of Pepsi which the owners kept at the back of the garage.

Mr Dickson sued the homeowner's insurance company, claiming that he had been the victim of kidnapping, starvation and mental torture. The jury awarded him $500,000 compensation.

Grammar | participle clauses for sequencing

3 Underline four examples of participle clauses used as sequencing devices in the website.

4 Read the sentences (1–6) and decide which action happened (or started) first (a or b).

1 Having taken two aspirin, I began to feel a little sick.
   a taking two aspirin **b** began to feel sick
2 Before going to bed, I have a glass of milk.
   a going to bed **b** have a glass of milk
3 After leaving home, he got a job in a circus.
   a leaving home **b** got a job in a circus
4 On hearing the news, I rushed out to tell my girlfriend.
   a hearing the news **b** rushed out
5 Having crashed his car, Gerry had to come by taxi.
   a coming by taxi **b** crashed his car
6 While waiting for the train, I noticed a small child crying on the platform.
   a waiting for the train **b** noticed a child

5 Rewrite the sentences (1–8) using the words in brackets.

Karl took the test then he went out to celebrate. (taken)
Having taken the test, Karl went out to celebrate.

1 Dave told his best friend before he announced the news to his colleagues. (having)

_____

2 He got up and went into the village to get some food. (after)

_____

3 They went to bed after they had watched the midnight movie. (going)

_____

4 Surinda was watching TV when she heard a strange sound. (while)

_____

5 Before we went to the computer shop we read lots of consumer reports. (reading)

_____

6 Jackie had to get a taxi because she missed the bus. (having)

_____

7 My uncle went to America and started a new business. (gone)

_____

8 The kids usually do their homework and then watch TV for an hour. (doing)

_____

Pronunciation | consonant clusters (2)

6 **a** Think about the consonant clusters at the end of each word and circle the odd-one-out in each group.

1 *against / evidence / insurance*
2 *clients / punishments / products*
3 *first / suspects / scientist*
4 *against / insurance / sentenced*
5 *punishments / suspects / products*
6 *next / context / clients*

b 🔊 29 Listen and check your answers. Then repeat the words.

Listening

1 **a** 🔊 30 Cover the audioscript. Listen to a radio programme and choose the best answers.

1 The radio programme is probably designed for …
   - **a** lawyers.
   - **b** 16- to 18-year-olds.
   - **c** young children.

2 How many guests will there be on the programme?
   - **a** none
   - **b** one
   - **c** more than one

3 Emily says the majority of lawyers work …
   - **a** in court.
   - **b** for criminals.
   - **c** in offices.

4 Divorce is part of …
   - **a** civil law.
   - **b** criminal law.
   - **c** court.

5 Emily thinks the most important quality of a barrister is …
   - **a** self-confidence.
   - **b** communication.
   - **c** a good memory.

b Listen again and complete the sentences.

1 There's a factsheet that you can _____ from the website.

2 Emily will help listeners to _____ the mysteries of the legal profession.

3 Barristers present a case for the prosecution or _____ the accused.

4 Only a small _____ of lawyers work in court in England.

5 What _____ qualities do you think a good barrister needs?

6 You've got to _____ you know what you're doing.

c Complete the sentences with words and phrases from exercise 1b.

1 I am writing this letter _____ the board of directors.

2 You're very tanned. You _____ you've been somewhere sunny.

3 I'm going to _____ some MP3 songs from the Internet.

4 This isn't the _____ behaviour I expect from someone like you.

5 Can you help me _____ these cables, they are all jumbled up.

6 You should try to have a large _____ of vegetables in your diet.

Voice: It's three o'clock and time for this week's edition of *Job Spotlight* with Zack Desmond.

Zack: Hello everyone and welcome once again to Job Spotlight. In today's programme we'll be looking at job opportunities in the legal profession. From your letters and emails I know this is a career that a lot of you are considering, so we've also put together a factsheet which you can download from our website. Now, as usual we have several guests here to help us unravel some of the mysteries of this particular profession. My first guest in the studio today is top lawyer Emily Waterstone.

Emily: Hello.

Zack: Welcome to the programme, Emily. Now, you're a barrister, aren't you?

Emily: Yes, a criminal barrister.

Zack: Can you tell us exactly what a barrister does?

Emily: I'll do my best. Actually, I think most people are familiar with barristers from TV and films. We're the people who stand up in court and present the case for the prosecution or on behalf of the accused, that's the person accused of a crime.

Zack: Don't all lawyers do that?

Emily: Not really. In England only a small proportion of lawyers work in court. Most lawyers work in offices – helping people buy houses, make their wills, get divorces – that kind of thing.

Zack: You said you were a criminal barrister. Does that mean you work for criminals?

Emily: No, not exactly. It means I work in criminal law rather than civil law.

Zack: So, what's the difference?

Emily: Well, criminal law is to do with actual crimes – murder, arson, robbery and so on. Civil law isn't about crimes at all – it's the law that governs things like contracts, inheritance, business, things like that.

Zack: So, you wouldn't be able to help me if I wanted to get a divorce.

Emily: I'm afraid not. Well, not unless divorce suddenly became a crime!

Zack: Right. Now for our listeners who are thinking about becoming barristers, what sort of qualities do you think a good barrister needs?

Emily: The main one is self-confidence I think. You've got to look like you know what you're doing. And communication is very important, especially in court.

Zack: I suppose a good understanding of human nature comes in useful.

Emily: Yes, and a good memory helps, too.

Zack: OK. Let's talk about the training you need to do …

Grammar | deduction: present and past

2 Match the questions (1–8) with the most appropriate answers (a–h).

1 Why didn't she pass the test? ☐
2 Why isn't she at work today? ☐
3 Why is she going to marry him? ☐
4 Why did she get an A+ in the test? ☐
5 Why did she do that job? ☐
6 Why is she divorcing him? ☐
7 Why didn't she say hello to me? ☐
8 Why is she so late? ☐

a She might be sick.
b She might have got lost.
c She can't be in love any more.
d She couldn't have seen you.
e She might have needed the money.
f She can't have done enough revision.
g She must be in love.
h She must have done lots of work.

3 Rewrite the underlined sentences using suitable forms of *must, might, can't* or *couldn't*.

The plants look very healthy. Someone is definitely watering them.

Someone must be watering them.

1 I'm sure he's at home. I can see the light on in his bedroom.

_____

2 I'm sure they haven't left the country. They don't have passports.

_____

3 My car's making a strange noise. Perhaps it needs a service.

_____

4 Their flat is empty. I'm certain they have left already.

_____

5 She definitely isn't guilty. She's a very honest person.

_____

6 Emma isn't here. Perhaps she didn't receive the invitation.

_____

7 Where's your umbrella? I'm absolutely sure you forgot to bring it.

_____

8 My mobile phone isn't working. Perhaps the battery is flat.

_____

4 Read the situation and complete the sentences (1–7) using *must, might* or *can't (have)*.

Last night £50,000 was stolen from the safe of Western United Bank. None of the doors or locks were broken so the police think somebody working in the bank stole the money. There were no fingerprints on the safe door, but the police found a cigarette end on the floor near the safe. No one is allowed to smoke in the bank. Only four members of staff have keys to the safe: Mr Briggs, the manager, Jennifer, the assistant manager, Darren, the chief cashier and Lauren, the mortgage advisor. Mr Briggs was at home with his wife all last night. His wife confirms this. Jennifer says she was at home, but she lives alone. Lauren isn't here at the moment; she is in the middle of a two-week holiday in Thailand. Darren says he was at home. He lives with his parents. His mother says he was at home all night, except when he went outside to take the dog for a walk at midnight.

1 The money _____ been stolen by a member of staff because none of the locks were broken.
2 It _____ be Lauren because she is on holiday.
3 It _____ been Mr Briggs, Jennifer, Darren or Lauren because they have keys to the safe.
4 There was a cigarette end on the floor, so the thief _____ be a smoker.
5 It _____ been Mr Briggs because he was at home with his wife all night.
6 Jennifer _____ be guilty because she can't prove she was at home last night.

Vocabulary | compound adjectives

5 Complete the sentences using compound adjectives.

1 Mr Lockwood is 50 years old.
   Mr Lockwood is _____
2 Wooden buildings are dangerous because they can catch fire.
   Wooden buildings are dangerous because they aren't _____
3 He should wear smart clothes to a job interview.
   When you go to a job interview, you should be
   _____
4 They caught the thief as he was taking the money from the till.
   The thief was caught _____
5 I never know what to say when I meet new people.
   When I meet new people I'm often _____
   _____

Pronunciation | compound adjectives

6 **a** Listen and check the answers to exercise 5. Underline the part of each compound adjective which has the main stress.

b 🌐 31 Listen again and repeat the sentences.

Reading

1 **a** Read the text quickly. Which statement is correct?

1 It summarises the complete plot and characters of *The Hound of the Baskervilles*.

2 It describes Conan Doyle's career, using *The Hound of the Baskervilles* as an example.

3 It explains the background to *The Hound of the Baskervilles* and gives the main points of the story.

b Read the text again and write true (T) or false (F).

1 *The Hound of the Baskervilles* was originally a series of magazine stories. ☐

2 People believe that a hound has killed Sir Charles Baskerville. ☐

3 Sir Charles was Henry Baskerville's uncle. ☐

4 Henry Baskerville comes to see Sherlock Holmes. ☐

5 Dr Mortimer is a friend of Sherlock Holmes. ☐

6 Dr Mortimer has some shocking new evidence about the mystery. ☐

7 Sherlock Holmes believes in scientific explanations. ☐

8 Holmes and Watson immediately solve the mystery. ☐

c Find the words (1–8) in the text. Decide if they are verbs, nouns or adjectives and match them with the definitions (a–h).

1 cliff-hanger ☐
2 curse ☐
3 beast ☐
4 estate ☐
5 heir ☐
6 consult ☐
7 inquest ☐
8 rational ☐

a (n) an animal (especially a wild or dangerous animal)

b (n) a court case which examines the causes of a person's death

c (v) ask for advice from an expert

d (n) a promise or legend that something terrible will happen

e (n) a large area of land with a house belonging to one person or family

f (adj) scientific and logical

g (n) an exciting development in a plot that makes the reader want to know more

h (n) somebody who inherits land or money when a relative dies

Sherlock Holmes and the Hound of the Baskervilles

① *The Hound of the Baskervilles* is one of the most famous and admired detective stories ever written. Published in 1901 and 1902, it originally appeared in nine monthly instalments in *The Strand* magazine. Like Dickens's serialised novels of the same era, each instalment ended with a suspenseful 'cliff-hanger' that kept author Arthur Conan Doyle's audience clamouring for more.

② In the story, the old and noble Baskerville family is threatened by a curse: 'A great, black beast, shaped like an enormous wild dog or hound, yet larger than any hound that has ever been seen' terrorises and kills any family member who comes to live at the Baskerville estate. As the story opens, the hound seems to have claimed its latest victim, Sir Charles Baskerville. Sir Charles's nephew, Henry, the new heir to the estate, is about to take up residence the next day. A friend of the family, Dr Mortimer, comes to consult the famous Sherlock Holmes in his rooms at 221b Baker Street, though he admits he doesn't know if the case is more suitable 'for a detective or a priest'. The first instalment of the novel originally ended as Dr Mortimer explains:

③ '... *One false statement was made by Barrymore at the inquest. He said that there were no traces upon the ground round the body. He did not observe any. But I did – a short distance away, but fresh and clear.*'

'*Footprints?*'

'*Yes, footprints.*'

'*A man's or a woman's?*'

Dr Mortimer looked strangely at us for an instant, and his voice sank almost to a whisper as he answered: 'Mr Holmes, they were the footprints of a gigantic hound!'

④ Into this atmosphere of ancient secrets, deadly curses and supernatural beasts comes the supremely rational Sherlock Holmes – a man described by his friend Watson as 'the most perfect reasoning and observing machine the world has ever seen'. Piece by piece Holmes and Watson solve the mystery and find the culprit. In the end, they reassure the characters in the novel (as well as Conan Doyle's Victorian readers), that behind the threat of a supernatural 'hound of hell' is a perfectly scientific explanation.

Grammar | relative clauses

2 Match the statements (1–8) with the explanations (a or b).

1 We stayed in the only hotel in the town which had a sea view.

2 We stayed in the only hotel in the town, which had a sea view.

   a There were several hotels but only one had a view of the sea. ☐

   b There was only one hotel in the town. ☐

3 My sister, who lives in Paris, has just had a baby.

4 My sister who lives in Paris has just had a baby.

   a I have several sisters and one of them lives in Paris. ☐

   b I only have one sister. ☐

5 All the students, who can speak French, were invited to the party.

6 All the students who can speak French were invited to the party.

   a All of the students were invited to the party. ☐

   b Some of the students were invited to the party. ☐

7 The cinema, which is opposite the station, is going to become a nightclub.

8 The cinema which is opposite the station is going to become a nightclub.

   a There is only one cinema in our town. ☐

   b There is more than one cinema in our town. ☐

3 Choose the correct words in *italics*. Sometimes both may be correct.

1 Mrs Kendrick, *that/who* used to be my teacher, has just retired.

2 Is this the new phone *that/which* you were telling me about?

3 The prisoner, who is *23, was/23 was* given a suspended sentence.

4 I've taken back the library book *you/that you* lent me last week.

5 This is the house *where/which* Mozart was born.

6 We had ice cream, *which/that* I love, for dessert.

7 He wrote a book *sold/that sold* over a million copies.

8 Dr Joseph Bell was the man *who/that* inspired Arthur Conan Doyle.

4 Complete the sentences with relative clauses using the information from the box. Add commas and relative pronouns if necessary.

> We met the girl on holiday.   The hospital is very old.
> It was elected last year.   Her boyfriend lives in Athens.
> ~~She is Spanish.~~   We stayed in the hotel last summer.
> He was Scottish.   I'm living in that house.
> I saw that film yesterday.

John's sister-in-law, *who is Spanish*, is training to be an opera singer.

1 Miranda's boyfriend _____ is a doctor.

2 The house _____ is over a hundred years old.

3 Arthur Conan Doyle _____ was born in 1859.

4 The government _____ has introduced a new tax.

5 Our local hospital _____ is about to be closed down.

6 The girl _____ is coming to stay next weekend.

7 Spielberg's new film _____ was fantastic.

8 The hotel _____ had a heated swimming pool.

How to... | start, move on and finish a discussion

5 Complete the conversation using the words from the box.

> agreed   come   for   have   individually   like
> on   start   think   what

A: So, what do we (1) _____ to decide?

B: We have to decide who is the best fictional detective: Sherlock Holmes, Miss Marple or Inspector Morse.

A: Why don't we start by talking about them (2) _____ , first?

B: OK. Shall we (3) _____ with Sherlock Holmes?

C: Yes. Let's go (4) _____ it.

A: So, moving (5) _____ to Miss Marple. I think she's the most interesting character.

C: But she isn't a real detective, is she? She's just an amateur.

A: I suppose so. Let's (6) _____ back to her later.

B: OK. I'd (7) _____ to go back to Sherlock Holmes.

A: So, I think we've (8) _____ on everything. Sherlock Holmes is the best detective.

B: Yes. (9) _____ else do we have to decide?

C: Nothing. I (10) _____ that's it.

Review and consolidation unit 9

Participle clauses

1 Choose the correct words in *italics*.

1 Before *leaving/left*, he gave me a business card.
2 Having *seeing/seen* the film myself, I wouldn't recommend it.
3 *At/On* arriving at the airport, the tourist group were met by the travel agent.
4 *After/Before* taking the tablets I felt a lot better – they were very effective.
5 Having opened the door, she *runs/ran* into the garden.
6 Before *booking/booked* the holiday, we did a lot of research.
7 While *lived/living* in York, she made many friends.
8 *To have/Having* taken the express train, Derek arrived in plenty of time.
9 On *the finish/finishing* his speech, the politician got a round of applause.
10 Having *learned/being learned* Spanish at school, I was able to communicate on holiday.

Deduction: present and past

2 Write the phrases (a–l) in the dialogue. Two of the phrases are not needed.

a	can't be	g	might have seen
b	can't have done	h	must be
c	might be in	i	mustn't be
d	might be on	j	must be stuck
e	might be here	k	must have done
f	might have forgotten	l	must have left

A: Where's Harry? He was supposed to be here.
B: He (1) _____ in traffic. I heard there was an accident on the motorway this morning.
A: No, he (2) _____ . He's coming by train.
B: Oh, I didn't know. He (3) _____ the 10:40.
A: I'm sure he said he was coming earlier.
B: Well, why don't you phone him?
A: I've just tried, but there's no answer.
B: He (4) _____ a tunnel – there's no signal.
A: There are no tunnels going to his house.
B: Well, he (5) _____ his phone at home.
A: No, he (6) _____ that, he never goes anywhere without it!
B: Are you sure? You know how forgetful he is.
A: He (7) _____ to take it with him.
B: How about calling his flatmate, Carmen? She (8) _____ him leave this morning.
A: I'm not sure. I don't want to disturb her.
B: Don't panic. He (9) _____ at any moment.
A: You're right. Oh, there's someone at the door.
B: That (10) _____ him!

Relative clauses

3 Find the mistakes in six of these sentences and correct them. Add relative pronouns and commas where necessary.

1 I've got a brother and two sisters – my brother that works in Cardiff is an opera singer.
2 Jenny of who I told you about is getting married.
3 The house we saw is worth over €1 million.
4 The children didn't pass the test had to retake it.
5 Our car which, we bought last year has been stolen, from our garage.
6 I've seen a lot of films recently – the film was on TV last night was absolutely fascinating.
7 Pilar, who guided us around town, is a real expert on Spanish history.
8 My husband, which you met last week has been promoted, to the Los Angeles office.

4 Use defining and non-defining relative clauses to make each numbered pair of sentences into one sentence.

1 The house has been sold. I used to live there.
2 It belonged to an old lady. The old lady died.
3 When I was young the old lady allowed me to play in her garden. The old lady used to be a schoolteacher.
4 The garden had lots of lemon trees. The garden was huge.
5 I used to pick the lemons from the trees. The trees grew there.
6 The old lady used the lemons to make lemonade. I had picked the lemons.

1 *The house where I used to live has been sold.*
2 _____
3 _____
4 _____
5 _____
6 _____

How to...

5 Choose the correct words in *italics*.

1 You'll never *consider/believe* what happened!
2 Let's talk about them *individually/individual*.
3 Did I *talk/tell* you about what happened?
4 It's not important. Let's come back *of/to* it later.
5 She's getting married. *Must/Can* you believe it?
6 I think we've agreed *on/for* everything.

Crime, law and insurance

6 Use the clues to complete the crossword.

1 That wasn't an accidental fire, it was ____ .
2 The police found him because he left his ____ on the weapon.
3 We filed an insurance ____ after our suitcase was stolen.
4 The murderer was given a ____ of 25 years in jail.
5 The ____ saw him set fire to the building.
6 The prisoner wasn't sent to jail, he was given a ____ sentence.
7 $25 million was stolen in the bank ____ .
8 In order to ____ someone you need to convince a jury of their guilt.
9 The police ____ several suspects at dawn this morning.
10 A ____ scientist examined the scene of the crime.
11 My car insurance ____ went up by 20% this year.
12 'I didn't do it – I'm completely ____ ,' she cried.
13 After the car crash we decided to ____ the other driver for compensation.
14 The main piece of ____ at the trial was a photo from a closed-circuit TV camera.
15 Perpetrators of ____ crime often go on to commit more serious offences.
16 The ____ stole my handbag while I was dancing.
17 My sister was the ____ of a robbery yesterday.
18 The criminal had to pay a ____ of $500.
19 Credit card ____ is one of the fastest-growing crimes.

Compound adjectives

7 Match each situation/description (1–8) with a suitable compound adjective (a–h).

1 She's stubborn and never listens to advice. ☐
2 He told us a spaceship had landed in the garden. ☐
3 The presents were covered in nice paper. ☐
4 When he met the president, Danny couldn't think of anything to say. ☐
5 Arturo is 48 and his wife is 43. ☐
6 Elena usually wears a smart suit to work. ☐
7 The police found the man with the stolen camera hidden under his jacket. ☐
8 Whatever the situation, these special doors will not burn. ☐

a gift-wrapped   e red-handed
b well-dressed   f tongue-tied
c pig-headed   g middle-aged
d fire-proof   h far-fetched

News headlines

8 Read the headlines and write true (T) or false (F).

AC Milan bids for top Portuguese player

BBC to axe top comedy show

Ministers clash over immigration

French Actress quits Hollywood

Prime Minister backs strikers

CHILDREN RESCUED FROM HOTEL BLAZE

Oscar-winning director in divorce drama

Government aid for homeless rises 25%

1 AC Milan has bought a new football player. ☐
2 The BBC will cancel a popular comedy show. ☐
3 Ministers disagree about immigration. ☐
4 A French actress has left Hollywood. ☐
5 The Prime Minister wants the strikers to go back to work. ☐
6 Firefighters have rescued some children from a hotel fire. ☐
7 An award-winning director is making a film about a divorce. ☐
8 The government says a quarter of homeless people have a disease. ☐

Listening

1 **a** 🔘 32 Cover the audioscript. Listen to the radio programme and choose the best summary.

1 The extract is a book review.

2 The extract is an interview with a writer.

3 The extract is about a famous French hypnotist.

b Listen again and use the information to complete the notes on Franz Mesmer's life. Write one word or number in each gap.

1734	born in (1) _____
1766	(2) _____ as a doctor from (3) _____ university started using (4) _____ on sick patients
1777	moved to (5) _____ . became famous treating French (6) _____ , he even treated the (7) _____ . he cured people but he also (8) _____ them.
1785	he was (9) _____ to go back to Germany.
(10) _____	he died

c Match the words and phrases (1–8) with the things they refer to (a–d). Then listen again to check your answers.

1 quite unique ☐

2 a kind of magic ☐

3 a great showman ☐

4 a recently discovered phenomenon ☐

5 were treated by Mesmer ☐

6 surprisingly effective ☐

7 like theatrical displays ☐

8 gullible ☐

a Franz Anton Mesmer

b Mesmer's treatments of patients

c French aristocrats

d magnetism

AUDIOSCRIPT

A: This week's biography choice is Mesmer – The Original Hypnotist. It is the story of Franz Anton Mesmer, the 18th-century scientist who is often regarded as the founder of hypnotism. With me in the studio is its author, Alexander Bond. Alexander, can I start by asking you what attracted you to this character?

B: Yes. Well, I've always been interested in hypnotists and I wanted to find out how hypnotism first started, so obviously that led me to Franz Mesmer.

A: Now, Mesmer is quite unique, isn't he?

B: Yes. He's one of the very few people whose name has become an English verb.

A: As in 'to be mesmerised by something' ...

B: Exactly. And that shows just how influential and important he was.

A: He was French, wasn't he?

B: Actually he was born in Germany, in 1734. And he studied medicine in Austria – at the University of Vienna, in fact.

A: So how did he first become famous?

B: Well, after he qualified as a doctor in 1766 he started doing experiments with magnets. Magnetism was a recently discovered phenomenon but it wasn't properly understood. People saw metal objects flying towards each other and it seemed to be a kind of magic. Anyway, Mesmer started applying magnets to his sick patients ...

A: To sick people?

B: Yes. In fact, it was surprisingly effective. Lots of his patients got better and Mesmer soon became the best-known doctor in Vienna. But the other doctors resented his success and forced him to move to Paris in 1777.

A: And that's where he became really famous?

B: Yes. Paris was pretty much the centre of European culture at the time, and the French were fascinated by Mesmer and his magnetic cures. Many members of the French aristocracy were treated by him. Even King Louis XVI became one of his patients. But then Mesmer was a great showman, his treatments were more like theatrical displays, so as well as curing people he entertained them.

A: But how did it work?

B: Well, we think that what he was really doing was hypnotising people. From detailed descriptions written at the time it seems he probably used the power of hypnotism to convince his patients they were feeling better.

A: He must have made a lot of money from those gullible French aristocrats!

B: Yes, he made a fortune. But his success didn't last for long. He failed to cure some influential members of French society and in 1785 he was forced to go back to Germany.

A: Did he carry on his medical work there?

B: Not really. But he had a happy and contented retirement. And he lived until 1815.

Grammar | reflexive pronouns

2 Complete the sentences with the correct words.

1 They've got an oven that cleans _____ .
   a himself   b itself   c them

2 Our teacher told _____ to do exercise 3.
   a ourselves   b we   c us

3 Successful team work depends on people helping _____ .
   a each other   b ourself   c each others

4 When he went on holiday David took his computer with _____ .
   a itself   b himself   c him

5 I hurt _____ when I was lifting a heavy suitcase.
   a myself   b me   c my

6 Emma sat down and relaxed _____ 20 minutes.
   a her for   b herself for   c for

7 The children really enjoyed _____ on the rollercoaster.
   a themselves   b itself   c each other

8 We couldn't afford builders so we decided to build the house _____ .
   a myself   b each other   c ourselves

9 It's very important to concentrate _____ you are driving.
   a while   b yourself while   c yourselves

10 At the end of the presentations, I want you to give _____ marks out of ten.
   a themselves   b each other   c you

3 Rewrite the sentences using reflexive pronouns or *each other*.

Janna looked at her reflection in the mirror.

Janna looked at herself in the mirror.

1 Darren cut his hand while he was gardening.

   _____

2 I made the cake without anyone's help.

   _____

3 We've made all the arrangements. No one helped us.

   _____

4 Mandy sent a text message to Sylvia and Sylvia sent one to Mandy.

   _____

5 My central heating turns on automatically if the temperature drops.

   _____

6 The Bensons often send packages to their home address when they are abroad.

   _____

7 Did you paint this picture on your own?

   _____

8 Isabel doesn't work for anybody else. She's self-employed.

   _____

Pronunciation | stress: reflexive pronouns

4 **a** Complete the sentences with reflexive pronouns. Then underline the part of the reflexive pronoun which is stressed.

1 They spent a lot of money on the production, but the show _____ is disappointing.

2 I don't want to speak to the agent. I want to speak to the owners _____ .

3 No, you misunderstood. I didn't paint it _____ – I got the decorators to do it.

4 I insist on speaking to the manager _____ , not his assistant!

b 🔘 33 Listen and check.

How to... | talk about beliefs and opinions

5 Find the mistakes in each of these sentences and correct them.

1 Are you in favour that the law against smoking in restaurants?

2 I'm quite sceptic that anyone can read another person's mind.

3 My friend is reckons there are ghosts in his house.

4 He's convenienced that the government is lying to us.

5 The police suspect of the murderer knew the victim.

6 I'm against give money to beggars.

7 I've always believed it hypnotism is a waste of time.

8 To be honest, I have my doubt about his intentions.

Reading

1 a Read the newspaper article quickly and choose the best summary.

1 Artificial smells haven't lived up to expectations.

2 Artificial smells have huge potential for business.

3 Banks hope artificial smells will increase their profits.

b Read the article again and write true (T) or false (F).

1 Dale Air has produced an artificial 'smell of money' for Barclays Bank. ☐

2 The bank is having problems with its air conditioning systems. ☐

3 It is difficult to isolate the real smell of money. ☐

4 Shoppers are aware of the effect smells have on their spending. ☐

5 The smell of coconuts seems to encourage people to buy holidays. ☐

6 Cafés often put coffee machines near the entrance. ☐

7 The human sense of smell is highly developed. ☐

8 Most of the scientific problems of producing artificial smells have now been solved. ☐

c Find the following words and phrases in the article.

1 a compound adjective to describe bread which has just been made

_____

2 an adjective meaning the opposite of *pessimistic* _____

3 a phrasal verb which means *to collect or attract something*

_____

4 a compound noun that describes a machine used to store money in a shop _____

5 an adverb we use when something is done in a clever and almost invisible way _____

6 a scientific phrase which refers to the parts of the body we smell things with

_____

7 an adjective made from the verb *to evoke* _____

8 a verb which means *to control something and use it for your own benefit* _____

The Smell of Money

For many years large supermarkets have been encouraging us to spend money by pumping the smell of freshly-baked bread into their stores. Now Dale Air, a leading firm of aroma consultants, has been approached by Barclays Bank to develop suitable artificial smells for their banks. Researchers have suggested that surrounding customers with the 'smell of money' will encourage them to feel relaxed and optimistic and give them added confidence in the bank's security and professionalism.

But before a smell can be manufactured and introduced into banks' air conditioning systems it must be identified and chemically analysed, and this has proved to be difficult. The problem is that banknotes and coins tend to pick up the smell of their surroundings. So cash that has been sitting in a cash register at a fishmonger's will smell of fish, and banknotes used to pay for meals in restaurants will tend to smell of food.

It may be a challenge, but aroma experts have little doubt that the use of artificial smells can be an effective form of subconscious advertising. Lunn Poly, a British travel company, introduced the smell of coconuts into its travel agencies and saw a big increase in spending by holiday makers. Many cafés now have electric dispensers that release the smell of freshly roasted coffee near their entrances, subtly encouraging customers to come in and have a drink or snack. Even prestige car maker Rolls-Royce has been spraying the inside of its cars to enhance the smell of the leather seats.

'The sense of smell is probably the most basic and primitive of all human senses,' explains researcher Jim O'Riordan. 'There is a direct pathway from the olfactory organs in the nose to the brain.' It is certainly true that most people find certain smells incredibly evocative, stirring memories and feelings in a way that few other stimulants can rival. It is a phenomenon marketing consultants have long recognised, but until recently have been unable to harness. 'We've made great progress but the technology of odour production is still in its infancy,' says O'Riordan. 'Who knows where it will take us.'

Vocabulary | advertising

2 Label the texts/words (1–3) using words from the box. Not all the words are needed.

publicity   brands   advertisement   trailer   marketing
target market   slogan

1 _____

'You deserve the best'

Siemens
Sony
Boeing
Rolls-Royce

2 _____

Married women living in the United States between the ages of 30 and 45 with annual incomes in excess of $30,000.

3 _____

Grammar | conditional structures (2): with conjunctions

3 Complete the second sentence so that it means the same as the first.

You can put on the life jacket, but only if there is an emergency.

Don't put on the life jacket *underline there is an emergency.*

1 What will you do if you fail the exam?
   Supposing you _____

2 It doesn't matter whether you water them or not, palm trees won't grow in Sweden.
   Even if you _____

3 We'll give you a place on the course if you pass the entrance test.
   Provided you _____

4 You can come to the party, but only if you have a written invitation.
   You can't come to the party _____

5 Only use the generator if there is a power failure.
   Don't use the generator _____

6 We will give you a guarantee if you pay by credit card.
   Provided _____

7 If the neighbours complain, you can't have a party.
   Unless _____

8 If you show us a receipt, we can give you a refund.
   As long as _____

4 Find the mistakes in the sentences and correct them. Think about the meaning as well as the grammar.

1 Provided you pay for the tickets, I went to the concert with you.

2 We'll have to go by taxi unless you can't borrow your father's car.

3 Supposing he doesn't arrive, what did you do?

4 As long that I work overtime, I can have an extra week's holiday.

5 You can't use a credit card at a cash machine unless you don't have a PIN number.

6 Even if you begged me, I would lend you my iPhone.

7 I stay here as long as you need me.

8 We'll organise your visa provided you would supply us with the correct documents.

How to... | persuade someone to do something

5 **a** Complete the conversation with words from the box.

| come | deserve | fun | go | just | lose |
| regret | sure | supposing | treat | | |

Ali: I feel like doing something special this evening. How about trying the new ice-skating rink in town?

Karl: Oh, I'm not (1) _____ .

Ali: (2) _____ on. I'm sure it'll be (3) _____ .

Karl: I've never been ice-skating before. I'll probably be useless at it.

Ali: Well, (4) _____ you try it just once – just to find out?

Karl: I don't know.

Ali: What have you got to (5) _____ ?

Karl: A lot! I could fall over and break an arm!

Ali: Oh, don't be a baby. We should (6) _____ do it!

Karl: And it's probably quite expensive to get in.

Ali: So what? Let's (7) _____ ourselves. We (8) _____ it. And you might be really good at skating – I mean, you're pretty good at most sports.

Karl: Do you think so?

Ali: Yes. Come on. I'm sure you won't (9) _____ it.

Karl: Oh, OK. Let's (10) _____ for it then.

b 🔵 34 Listen and check your answers.

Pronunciation | intonation: sounding enthusiastic

6 🔵 35 Listen to these extracts from the dialogue in exercise 5 and underline the words which are stressed. Then repeat the sentences.

1 Come on, I'm sure it'll be fun.

2 What have you got to lose?

3 Let's treat ourselves.

4 Come on, I'm sure you won't regret it.

5 OK, let's go for it then.

Reading

1 **a** Read the website quickly and decide if the statement is true or false.

- Most people on the forum have positive feelings about mini spy planes.

b Match the people with their ideas and opinions. Write H (Helen), D (Dieter), M (Mariusz) or C (Consuela):

1 Doesn't care about privacy. ☐
2 Wants to buy a mini spy plane. ☐
3 Is worried about how the authorities might use mini spy planes. ☐
4 Thinks mini spy planes are fun. ☐
5 Is frightened. ☐
6 Thinks there's nothing to worry about. ☐
7 Is worried that mini spy planes could be used in the workplace. ☐
8 Thinks it is wrong to film people without them knowing about it. ☐

c Find the words from the box in the website and use them to complete the sentences (1–6). Not all the words are needed.

> nightmare beam undetected
> receiver hypocrites fuss geek
> miniature surveillance immoral

1 My brother's a real computer _____ – he spends all his time on it and he knows all the jargon!
2 People who pretend to like you, then say bad things about you behind your back, are just _____ .
3 I think it's _____ to waste food when there are so many starving people in the world.
4 Please don't make such a _____ – you're embarrassing me.
5 Surinda's just bought a _____ radio – it's smaller than a postage stamp!
6 I lost my passport when I was abroad and the embassy was closed – it was a complete _____ !

Are 'insect' spy planes the new digital nightmare?

Scientists in Holland and the United States have been developing flying cameras so small that they are not much bigger than a dragonfly. Controlled by radio signals, these tiny 'insect planes' can fly almost anywhere, virtually undetected. They then beam high-definition colour pictures and sound to a receiver hundreds of metres away.

Is this the end of individual privacy? Has digital technology advanced so far that no part of our life is free from being recorded and watched by total strangers?

We asked for your views.

Helen, from Glasgow
I saw pictures of these tiny 'spy planes' on the news and it really scared me. I hate all those security cameras everywhere, but this is much worse. At least with the security cameras you can see them and you know they're recording you. But these things are so small they can hide anywhere. (1) _____ your boss put one somewhere in the office, you'd never know about it! Nowhere (2) _____ be private any more!

Dieter, from Berlin
People are such hypocrites! They put hundreds of photos and videos of themselves on the Internet, write blogs and lifelogs about what they are doing all the time – and then they complain when somebody takes photos of them! I think it's a lot of fuss about nothing. Nobody cares about privacy any more.

Mariusz, from Warsaw
I'm a bit of a geek and I love all these new high-tech toys! These miniature flying cameras look brilliant. I wish I (3) _____ have one to play around with. I'd send it into my friends' houses to find out what they say about me behind my back! That would be a lot of fun. If it (4) _____ on the market I'll definitely buy one.

Consuela, from Buenos Aires
Has anyone thought about how governments are (5) _____ use these tiny spy planes? I bet the army is (6) _____ to use them to spy on their enemies. Perhaps they are already using them. There's far too much surveillance these days and the government already knows way too much about our private lives. I think it's immoral and it should be illegal to take pictures of people or record them without their permission.

Vocabulary | verb phrases with *mind*

2 Complete the second sentence so that it means the same as the first, using an appropriate phrase with *mind*.

1 I'm going to tell him exactly what I think of him.
I'm going to _____ _____

2 I was going to buy a paper but I completely forgot about it.
I was going to buy a paper but it _____ _____

3 There's no more time, you have to make a decision now.
It's time to _____ _____

4 I was driving when suddenly I thought of a solution to that problem.
A solution to that problem _____ _____
while I was driving.

5 Miranda originally wanted to become a doctor but then she decided to become a vet.
At first Miranda wanted to become a doctor but she _____ _____

6 I can't concentrate on my work when people are talking in the background.
If people are talking in the background, I find it difficult to _____ _____ my work.

7 Have you ever considered emigrating to Canada?
Has emigrating to Canada ever _____ _____

8 Jenna's a vegetarian – I'll have to remember that when I'm cooking tonight's meal.
I know Jenna's a vegetarian and I'll have to _____ _____ while I'm cooking.

Grammar | futures (2)

3 Fill the gaps in the website on page 80 with words from the box.

> comes   could   going to
> intending   if   will

4 Tick (✓) the best explanation (a or b).

1 I'm taking my cousins to the theatre on Friday.
   a I've bought the tickets. ☐
   b I want to do this but I haven't bought the tickets yet. ☐

2 If I knew his number, I'd phone him.
   a I don't know his number. ☐
   b I used to know his number. ☐

3 I'm intending to take a long holiday.
   a I'm on holiday now. ☐
   b I'm planning a holiday for the future. ☐

4 If only we were rich.
   a We are rich. ☐
   b We aren't rich, but we'd like to be. ☐

5 I'm hungry. I think I'll get something out of the fridge.
   a I'm talking about tomorrow's lunch. ☐
   b I've just decided to do this. ☐

6 If I get a promotion, I'll move to a bigger flat.
   a I might get a promotion. ☐
   b I probably won't get a promotion. ☐

7 One day I'm going to do a part-time course on website design.
   a I'm talking about tomorrow evening. ☐
   b I talking about something I plan to do, but I haven't enrolled on a course yet. ☐

8 I wish I could join you on the beach.
   a I'd like to join you later, but I've got to finish my homework. ☐
   b I wasn't able to go to the beach yesterday. ☐

5 Choose the correct words in *italics*.

1

I have/I'll have a vegetarian pizza, please.

2

Don't worry, *you're sitting/ you'll sit* next to each other in the same row.

3

I wish I *will/could* afford to go there.

4

I'm in training. *I've decided/ I'm going to decide* to take part in the next marathon.

5

If you *didn't/don't* give me the loan, I'll take my business to another bank.

6

I'm *being/going to be* an astronaut when I grow up.

Reflexive pronouns

1 Find the mistakes in six of these sentences and correct them.

1 Emma cut her while doing the washing up.
2 Mike takes his laptop with himself when he goes on business trips.
3 Juanita and Mario phone each others every day.
4 I'm going to teach myself to play the violin.
5 To save money we painted our house ourself.
6 Mr and Mrs Wright decided to take their grandchildren with themselves when they went on holiday.
7 I have no objections to the product itself; it's the advertisement that annoys me.
8 I repaired me the broken chair.

Conditional structures (2): with conjunctions

2 Complete the sentences with the correct words.

1 I'll go to the party ____ you agree to come too.
  a unless b as long as c if not
2 If we ____ stuck in this traffic jam, we would be there by now.
  a didn't get b don't get c hadn't got
3 If the film hadn't ended so late, we ____ the last bus home.
  a would miss b wouldn't have missed
  c don't miss
4 We'll give you a refund ____ back the receipt.
  a provided you bring
  b provided you brought
  c unless you bring
5 ____ you miss the flight, what will you do?
  a Unless b Even if c Supposing
6 We'll stay at the big hotel ____ it isn't too expensive.
  a even if b as long as c unless
7 I couldn't answer that question ____ I wanted to.
  a even if b provided that
  c supposing
8 If we'd arrived earlier, we ____ the film stars arriving.
  a might see b saw c might have seen
9 You mustn't use that expensive mobile phone ____ it's a real emergency.
  a if b provided c unless
10 Darren ____ in the winning team if he hadn't broken his leg.
  a wasn't b could have been
  c can be

Futures (2)

3 Read the email. Choose the correct options in *italics*.

Hi Luka

I've been thinking about your suggestion about changing my course and (1) *I'll decide/I've decided* to follow your advice. I'm (2) *going to talk/talking* to my tutor sometime soon. If he (3) *will agree/agrees* to it, I'll be able to change to the media studies course next term. I'm sure it (4) *can/is going to* be much more interesting than the course I'm on now, and I'm (5) *determined/going to determine* to make a success of it.

How are things in Montreal? I wish I (6) *can/could* afford to fly there and spend some time with you. If I had the money (7) *I'd/I'll* come over and spend a weekend in Canada. It seems like ages since we last met! If only you (8) *don't/didn't* live so far away!

Have you made any plans for the New Year holiday yet? I've just bought my tickets and (9) *I'm taking/I'll take* the train to my grandparents' house. It's always fun visiting them.

Anyway, it's getting late and I think (10) *I'll finish/I'm finishing* now. I'll write again soon.

Siobhan XX

The power of the mind

4 Choose the correct words in *italics*.

1 Harold was knocked *subconscious/unconscious* by the falling tree.
2 Although I had never been there before I had a strong feeling of *sixth sense/déjà vu*.
3 I always *trust/believe* my intuition about new people I meet.
4 Before we left for the airport I had an awful *premonition/intuition* that something bad was about to happen.
5 It isn't really difficult to learn new skills – it's just a question of *brain/mind* over matter.
6 You need a lot of *premonition/willpower* to give up smoking.
7 My brother gets very stressed about his work – the doctor says it's his *subconscious/unconscious* fear of failure.
8 Hypnotists are experts at using the power of *persuasion/intuition*.

Advertising

5 Use the clues to complete the crossword.

1   A short film that tells us about a new feature film.
2   A short clever phrase used by advertisers or politicians.
3   A small visual image or symbol that represents a company.
4   A ____ break is a series of advertisements between TV programmes.
5   For this product our target ____ is teenagers.
6   Deciding where and how to sell products, how much to charge, etc.
7   Publicity that makes something seem important.
8   What ____ is it? Sony or Philips?
9   Pictures, words or a short film that tries to sell you a product.

Verb phrases with *mind*

6 Match the sentence halves.

1   I'm going to join the civil service – ☐
2   I told him exactly what I thought of him – ☐
3   I'm sorry I forgot to get you a present, I'm afraid ☐
4   I'm not going to buy that expensive phone after all – ☐
5   I'm finding it really difficult to do my work today – ☐
6   I can't think of a solution at the moment, I'm afraid ☐

a   I really spoke my mind.
b   nothing springs to mind.
c   I just can't keep my mind on it.
d   I've made up my mind.
e   it slipped my mind.
f   I've changed my mind.

Commonly misspelt words

7 Write the letters from the box in the words (1–10).

> cc   ea   ei   el   ell   il   iou   ou   ss   syc

1   int____igence
2   p____hologist
3   subconsc____s
4   th____r
5   responsib____ity
6   definit____y
7   chang____ble
8   nece____ary
9   gener____s
10 o____asionally

How to...

8 Rewrite the sentences using correct forms of the phrases from the box.

> to have always believed that
> to be sceptical about   to be fun
> to be convinced   ~~to have your doubts about~~
> to go for it   to be in favour of

Janet isn't really sure about this new job.
Janet has her doubts about this new job.

1   I am absolutely certain that Jimmy is guilty of the crime.
_____
_____

2   Emily supports the idea of longer prison sentences for criminals.
_____
_____

3   I think you should take the new job.
_____
_____

4   All my life I have had the opinion that people are basically honest.
_____
_____

5   I'm sure it will be really enjoyable!
_____
_____

6   I really don't completely trust or believe in hypnosis.
_____
_____

Unit 1 Connect

Lesson 1.1

Reading

1a

3

1b

1 dichotomy **2** wannabe **3** self-deluded **4** gasp **5** soaring **6** solely **7** homely **8** standing ovation **9** instant **10** tendency **11** prodigious **12** bemused

1c

1 Don't judge a book by its cover **2** It was a survival mechanism – early humans often needed to make life-or-death decisions. **3** She is from a small village near Glasgow. **4** Susan Boyle's appearance on *Britain's Got Talent*. **5** She wasn't good-looking, or in her teens or early 20s. **6** They were bemused, and thought she would be embarrassing. **7** Her powerful, soaring voice. **8** However sophisticated we believe we are, we still make instant judgements based on appearances.

Grammar: overview (1): the present and future

2

1 'll try **2** 're going to see **3** exists **4** 'm using **5** 'll probably come / is probably going to come **6** closes **7** is going to be **8** visit **9** 'm watching **10** keep **11** 'm attending **12** will definitely be / is definitely going to be

Vocabulary | ways of speaking

3

1 GREET **2** GOSSIP **3** SPEAK **4** STUMBLE **5** COMPLIMENT **6** CHAT **7** SMALL **8** BOAST **9** MUMBLE

How to... | make a good first impression

4

1 Pleased **2** a pleasure **3** When did you move in **4** Have you lived here long **5** Really **6** sounds interesting **7** do you do **8** Are you **9** I know what you mean **10** really nice talking

Lesson 1.2

Listening

1a

3

1b

1 T **2** T **3** F **4** F **5** F **6** T **7** T **8** F

1c

1 author **2** tossing **3** tomb **4** swords **5** confined **6** grave stone **7** myths **8** linked

Grammar | overview (2): the past

2

1 was eating **2** hadn't been / had never been **3** passed **4** rained / was raining **5** had drunk **6** was released **7** had lost **8** met **9** were watching **10** revised / was revising

3

1 That restaurant's great – I **went / was** there last month. **2** ✓ **3** I **phoned** you three times. Where were you? **4** The doorbell rang while I **was having** a shower. **5** ✓ **6** It was our first visit – we **hadn't been / had never been** there before.

Vocabulary | making adjectives from nouns

4

1 artistic **2** responsible **3** skill **4** Jealousy **5** successful **6** lonely **7** frustrated **8** intellect

How to... | manage a conversation

5

1 e **2** a **3** b **4** d **5** c **6** f

Pronunciation | sounding tentative

6a

1 T **2** C **3** C **4** T

Lesson 1.3

Listening

1a

1 c **2** a **3** d **4** b

1b

1 The man **mainly** uses his phone to send text messages. **2** He **can't** use his phone at work. **3** The man **is annoyed by** people on the phone when he's on the train. **4** The woman thinks it's **sometimes** cheap / not expensive to make mobile calls. **5** Steve's mobile was **a bargain / cheap**. **6** John thinks Steve's new phone is **sophisticated**. **7** The customer **has** children. **8** If he isn't happy after 10 days, the customer can get a **refund**.

1c

1 on special offer **2** keep in touch **3** tracks **4** loads **5** non-stop **6** tariffs **7** drives me mad **8** cost a bomb **9** the really neat thing

Vocabulary | keeping in touch

2

1 S **2** D **3** D **4** S **5** S

Grammar | obligation and ability

3

1 don't have to **2** was able to **3** shouldn't **4** should **5** should have got **6** mustn't **7** should have tried **8** could / was able to **9** didn't have to pay **10** have to / must

4

1 You have **to** get a visa to work in the US. **2** We didn't **have** to pay cash because the hotel accepted credit cards. **3** ✓ **4** Carlos got lost – we should **have** given him a map. **5** ✓ **6** You should always wash your hands before eating. **7** ✓ **8** Is it true that you can **see** the Great Wall of China from space?

Pronunciation | connected speech (1)

5a

1 ✓ **2** ✓ **3** ✓ **4** (strong form) **5** ✓ **6** ✓ **7** ✓ **8** ✓ **9** ✓ **10** (strong form)

Review and consolidation unit 1

The present and future

1

1 Are you leaving **2** 'm meeting **3** is **4** 's getting **5** is she going to stay / will she stay **6** 'll take **7** lives **8** 'll ask **9** Are you catching **10** 're repairing

The past

2

1 met; was working **2** drove; had **3** hadn't seen **4** missed; got; had already left **5** arrived; was shining; took off; ran **6** made; got; had left **7** were sleeping; struck **8** had seen; knew; found

Obligation and ability

3

1 a ✓ b ✓ c ✗ **2** a ✗ b ✗ c ✓ **3** a ✗ b ✓ c ✗ **4** a ✓ b ✗ c ✗ **5** a ✓ b ✗ c ✓

How to...

4

1 e **2** c **3** f **4** b **5** a **6** d

Family/relationships

5

1 WIFE **2** BOYFRIEND **3** ACQUAINTANCE **4** CLOSE **5** COLLEAGUE **6** GET ON **7** HALF **8** IMPRESSION **9** FACE **10** SOULMATE **11** EYE **12** STEP

Phrasal verbs (relationships)

6

1 gets on **2** looked up to **3** Bringing up **4** have split up **5** show off **6** takes after **7** have fallen out **8** is going out with

Adjectives/nouns

7

1 lonely **2** intellectual **3** artistic **4** skill **5** successful **6** responsibility **7** jealous **8** important

Unit 2 Explore

Lesson 2.1

Reading
1a
2

1b
Suggested answers **1** How long have Chinese 'speed tourists' been coming to Germany? **2** How many tourists are expected to arrive this year? **3** What is it that tempts the Chinese tourists to drive on the *autobahns*? **4** How many kilometres of German motorways have no speed limit? **5** What make/type of car do the tour operators offer to the tourists? **6** What speed are these cars capable of? / How fast can these cars go? **7** How much does a six-day *autobahn* tour cost? **8** How many people die on China's roads each day?

1c
1 holidaymakers, travellers **2** motorways, highways (*autobahns*) **3** tour operators **4** virtually **5** mythical **6** undeterred

Grammar | Present Perfect Simple and Continuous
2
1 have been flocking **2** have added **3** have been bringing **4** have discovered **5** has been expanding **6** has not proved **7** have reacted **8** have been

3
1 No, I haven't paid for the shopping yet. **2** They've been swimming in the lake. **3** No, I've never been/gone there. **4** Yes, he's just come back from Miami Beach. **5** I've been following a strict diet for the last two months. **6** No, I've already done it. **7** Yes, she's been typing it since lunchtime. **8** Yes, I've been teaching karate for more than ten years. **9** I've been washing the floors all afternoon. **10** No, I haven't been a member since 2010.

Pronunciation | connected speech (2)
4a
1 ✓ **2** ✓ **3** ✓ **4** (strong form) **5** ✓ **6** ✓ **7** (strong form) **8** ✓

Vocabulary | describing situations and feelings
5
1 inspiring; inspired **2** annoyed; annoying **3** fascinating; fascinated **4** petrified; petrifying **5** daunting; daunted

Lesson 2.2

Reading
1a
1 f **2** c **3** g **4** e **5** a
1b
1 T **2** T **3** F **4** F **5** F **6** T **7** T **8** F

1c
Paragraph 1 centrally heated **Paragraph 2** sparsely populated **Paragraph 3** solidly built **Paragraph 4** well known **Paragraph 5** reasonably comfortable; well stocked

Vocabulary | weather
2

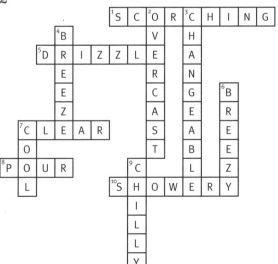

Pronunciation | connected speech: linking sounds
3b
1 /r/ **2** /w/ **3** /j/ **4** /j/ **5** /r/ **6** /w/ **7** /r/ **8** /j/

Grammar | questions
4
1 Who was she talking to? **2** Do you know if this is my seat? **3** Can you tell me how much it costs? **4** Where did they take the car? **5** Could I ask you to open the window? **6** How do you turn off the computer / How do you turn the computer off? **7** Are these the correct answers? **8** How long have you been working here?

5
1 Can you tell me what your email address is? **2** Could I ask you if/whether Graham Randall lives here? **3** Do you know if this is the correct platform for the train to Brighton? **4** I'd like to know which seats in the plane have the most legroom. **5** Can I ask you if/whether the doctor is available now? **6** Can you explain exactly where she lives? **7** Do you know how much the tickets cost? **8** Would you tell me who is in charge?

Lesson 2.3

Listening
1a
a 4 **b** 3 **c** 1 **d** 5 **e** 2
1b
a 5 **b** 4 **c** 2 **d** 3 **e** 1
1c
1 considered **2** uproot **3** intrigued by **4** grim **5** tempting **6** to be honest **7** obviously **8** opportunities

Grammar | modifying comparatives
2
1 quite **2** slightly **3** far more **4** far **5** as **6** lot **7** isn't **8** by **9** easily **10** a

3
1 Alvaro had by far **the best** results in the exam. **2** This exercise is **a bit** more difficult than the last one. **3** ✓ **4** I don't go to the gym as often **as** I used to. **5** The Mayback is easily the **most** expensive car BMW has ever made. **6** In the summer, Moscow can be much warmer than most people expect. **7** ✓ **8** If you want to pass the test, you'll have to answer the questions **a** lot faster. **9** ✓ **10** I'm **just as** tall as my sister. **11** Could you speak **a** little more slowly? I can't understand you. **12** ✓

Vocabulary | verb phrases about moving/travelling
4
1 g **2** c **3** f **4** a **5** h **6** e **7** d **8** b

Review and consolidation unit 2

Present Perfect Simple and Continuous
1
1 has been **2** has become **3** has been **4** has been leading / has led **5** has appeared / has been appearing **6** has had **7** helped **8** has given **9** has visited **10** have clearly influenced **11** met **12** spoke **13** has appeared **14** made **15** has only been doing/has only done

Questions
2
(line 1) Where did you go for your holidays?
(line 3) Who went on holiday with you?
(line 5) Can I ask what her name is?
(line 7) Could you tell me what she does for a living?
(line 11) Can you tell me if/whether she is British?
(line 13) How long has she lived here?
(line 15) I'd like to know where you met.
(line 19) Would you tell me how long you stayed in Florida?

Modifying comparatives
3
1 a, c **2** b, c **3** a, b **4** a, c **5** a **6** a, b, c **7** a, b **8** c

Exploring
4
1 independence → independent **2** shocked → shock **3** make → have **4** journey → travel **5** housesick → homesick **6** wonder → wander

Describing situations, feelings

5
1 WORRIED **2** CHALLENGING **3** FASCINATING **4** DISGUSTING
5 PETRIFIED **6** INSPIRED **7** FASCINATED **8** PETRIFYING **9** ANNOYING
10 DAUNTED

Weather

6
1 clear **2** cool **3** breezy **4** pour **5** humid **6** drizzle **7** scorching
8 calm **9** chilly **10** warm

Verb phrases about moving

7
1 moved **2** off **3** abroad **4** emigrated **5** around **6** set **7** home **8** off

Expressions with *go*

8
1 for **2** have **3** make **4** without **5** back **6** lengths **7** on **8** the

How to …

9
1 sooner **2** which **3** more **4** including **5** less

Unit 3 Old or new

Lesson 3.1

Listening

1a
1 458 **2** 1959 **3** directed **4** 1960 **5** 1961 **6** Spanish **7** actor **8** 1963
9 starring **10** 2004

1b
1 *Lawrence of Arabia* **2** *Spartacus* **3** *Ben Hur*
4 *Troy* and *Alexander* (and *Cleopatra*) **5** *Cleopatra* **6** *Gladiator*

1c
1 dormant **2** genre **3** golden age **4** sets **5** superb **6** alongside
7 a fortune **8** extras

How to... | engage your listener

2
1 b **2** e **3** a, d **4** c, f

Grammar | Past Perfect Simple and Continuous

3
1 had won **2** had earned **3** had been working **4** had spent
5 had never appeared **6** had begun **7** had been trying
8 had not been

4
(suggested answers) **1** she had missed the bus. **2** he had been
repairing his car. **3** had been playing computer games
4 she had already seen it.

5
1 had been working **2** hadn't seen **3** had been lying **4** hadn't done
5 had left **6** had been waiting **7** had been talking **8** hadn't driven

Vocabulary | time expressions

6
1 For the previous **2** since then **3** during **4** throughout
5 at that time **6** from that point on / after that **7** while
8 After that / from that point on

Lesson 3.2

Reading

1a
1 They are tiny shops that stay open late at night. **2** They are not
staffed by local people. **3** People from the Indian sub-continent.
4 Members of the owner's family work there. **5** They share in the profits.

1b
1 well-known **2** huge **3** city-dwellers **4** rarely **5** immigration **6** run
7 economics **8** source

Grammar | articles

2
1 – **2** the **3** The **4** – **5** – **6** The **7** an **8** a **9** – **10** the

3
1 ✓ **2** Janine and Mike have got **a** beautiful garden. **3** She'd been
living in Los Angeles since the 1980s. **4** ✓ **5** When I was young I
wanted to be **an** astronaut. **6** Let's have another look at **the** first one
they showed us. **7** I think **the** mobile phone is the greatest invention
ever. **8** ✓ **9** Rudolf's planning to study philosophy at university.
10 Have you got **a** double room with a sea view? **11** The Azores are in
the middle of **the** Atlantic Ocean. **12** ✓ **13** I love looking at **the** moon
at night. **14** This is **the** most exciting book I've read for a long time.
15 ✓

Pronunciation | connected speech: elision

4b
1 I had a lovely lunch at a little place on the corner of the high street.
2 Did you take a photo of the man in the straw hat? **3** The alligator
is one of the biggest reptiles in the Americas. **4** It's a fact that the
Republic of China will become one of the richest countries in the world
in the next twenty years. **5** A friend of ours is a doctor at the local
hospital.

Vocabulary | materials

5

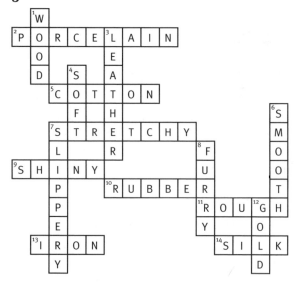

How to... | reach an agreement

6
1 take **2** point **3** say **4** you're **5** on

Lesson 3.3

Reading

1a
1 Zara **2** Shell **3** Gap **4** Shell **5** Nestlé **6** Shell **7** Coca-Cola **8** Zara
9 Gap **10** Coca-Cola

1b
1 beverages **2** manufacturer **3** non-alcoholic **4** founded
5 distributor **6** brands **7** worldwide **8** consumed

Pronunciation | speech units

2
Shell is a multinational company // famous for its petrol stations and
oil production facilities. // Founded by Marcus Samuel in London in
1833, // the company merged with the Royal Dutch group in 1907. //
Shell's international headquarters is now in the Hague, // Holland. //
Shell operates in 90 countries // and employs around 101,000 people.
// Shell generates sales in the region of 278 billion dollars from its
worldwide operations.

Grammar | adjectives and adverbs

3
1 When I have a bad headache all I want to do is lie down. **2** He
didn't work hard, so he was bound to fail the exam. **3** You're very
early; did you drive fast? **4** Anna is always expensively dressed in
designer outfits. **5** Some of these new computer games are incredibly
challenging. **6** It snowed heavily throughout our holiday. **7** He rudely
interrupted me in the middle of my speech. **8** Do you know them
well? **9** I'm definitely going to take the First Certificate Exam this
year. **10** The weather can be surprisingly hot in September.

4
1 reasonably priced 2 completely ruined 3 recently 4 hard 5 well
6 probably 7 nearly 8 unlikely 9 late 10 high

Vocabulary | verb phrases with *take*
5
1 c 2 c 3 a 4 a 5 c 6 b 7 c 8 a

Review and consolidation unit 3
Past Perfect Simple and Continuous
1
1 a 2 b 3 b 4 a 5 b 6 a 7 a 8 b

Articles
2
1 the most 2 Portsmouth 3 the railway 4 a tunnel 5 the longest
6 ships 7 the United States 8 the Atlantic 9 a ship 10 a propeller
11 Ambition 12 stubbornness

Adjectives and adverbs
3
1 lately → late 2 ✓ 3 general → generally 4 finely → fine
5 quick → quickly 6 hardly → hard 7 ✓ 8 interestingly → interesting
9 highly → high 10 definite → definitely

4
1 The professor treats all his students in a friendly way. 2 Isabel is
definitely the oldest student in our class. 3 I washed the sheets this
morning. 4 My brother sometimes forgets his PIN number. 5 Daniela
left her suitcase in the corner of the room. 6 The children stupidly
forgot to bring their swimming costumes. 7 He wasn't driving
dangerously, but he was going quite fast. 8 She has a warm and
caring personality.

Age and time expressions
5

		¹F						²P		³F	
⁴T	R	A	D	I	T	I	O	N	A	L
		S						I		S
		H						N		H
⁵P	R	E	V	I	O	U	S			I
		O						T		O
⁶A	N	⁷C	I	E	N	T		⁸D	U	R	I	N	G
N		E								A
T		N								B
I		T			⁹E	L	D	E	R	L	Y
Q		U								E
U		R								
E		Y								

Materials and describing objects
6a
1 e 2 g 3 f 4 d 5 a 6 c 7 b
6b
1 c 2 e 3 b 4 a 5 d

Verb phrases with *take*
7
1 away 2 in 3 stride 4 over 5 for 6 in 7 to 8 off

Making nouns
8
1 motherhood 2 Friendship 3 pianist 4 production 5 Happiness
6 arrangements

How to...
9
1 c 2 e 3 d 4 b 5 f 6 a

Unit 4 Work
Lesson 4.1
Listening
1a
1 actor 2 photographer 3 hotel receptionist 4 architect
1b
1 show off (b) 2 buzz (g) 3 line of work (e) 4 snowballed (d)
5 freelance (h) 6 a real handful (a) 7 a thing for (c) 8 in the blood (f)
1c
1 'm appearing 2 'll take 3 are going to live

Vocabulary | work
2
1 flexible working day. 2 does voluntary work 3 commuting.
4 work from home. 5 a workaholic. 6 paid employment.
7 a work-centred culture. 8 in the workplace.

Grammar | futures (1)
3
1 a 2 b 3 b 4 b 5 a 6 a 7 b 8 a

How to... | talk about future plans
4
1 in the next month or so. 2 in about an hour's time. 3 I'm not sure
yet but 4 I'm thinking about leaving 5 this coming October.
6 one possibility is to take the kids 7 they are about to announce
8 It all depends on the economic

Lesson 4.2
Reading
1a
1 It refers to the feelings people should have about the shocking amount
of waste in modern society. 2 It is significant because it weighs the
same as the amount of electrical equipment thrown away by an average
person in a lifetime. 3 It ends up in landfill sites or is incinerated.
1b
(**Any two of the following**)
Adjectives: shocking, extravagant, assorted, surprising, average,
sheer, electronic
Adverbs: dramatically, unnecessarily, currently
Body: teeth , eyes, ears
Electronics: televisions, mobile phones, satellite dishes, computer mice
Appliances: washing machines, fridges, vacuum cleaners, kettles,
microwaves
1c
1 discarded 2 commissioned 3 extravagant 4 high-tech 5 cabling
6 mice 7 encourage 8 currently 9 landfill sites 10 incinerated

Grammar | Future Perfect and Future Continuous
2
1 No, I'll be going in August instead. 2 Yes, he should have finished
it by then. 3 No, I'm afraid he'll be seeing another client then. 4 Yes,
we should have received planning permission by then. 5 Yes, they
will be staying with us from July to September. 6 No, I'll be working
at home all day tomorrow. 7 Pretty well. By the end of next month
we should have finished most of it. 8 Yes, she will have done it by
lunchtime at the latest.

3
1 will have finished 2 will have left 3 'll be lying 4 'll be bringing
5 will have arrived

Vocabulary | verb phrases about time
4
1 make → take 2 from time → of time 3 ✓ 4 time to murder → time to
kill 5 ✓ 6 for sparing → to spare 7 complete-time → full-time 8 ✓

How to... | make your point in a confident way
5
1 really 2 doubt 3 for 4 me 5 fact is

Pronunciation | stress: sounding sure
6b
1 I <u>understand</u> your point of view, I <u>really do</u>. 2 My <u>job</u> isn't as
satisfying as my <u>family</u> life, for <u>sure</u>. 3 The fact is I have a <u>very</u>
demanding job and I'm under a <u>lot</u> of pressure.

Lesson 4.3

Reading

1a

a 3 b 5 c 4 d 1 e 6 f 2

1b

1 sport **2** health **3** police **4** educational **5** military **6** corporate
7 health **8** military; sport

Grammar | verb patterns: -ing forms and infinitives

2

1 to work **2** taking **3** to send **4** to cut down **5** pressing **6** applying
7 to inform **8** to use **9** working **10** buying

3

1 Our teacher allowed us to leave early. **2** My parents encouraged me to learn a musical instrument. **3** Danny persuaded the check-in clerk to upgrade him to business class. **4** The doctor advised Sara to lose some weight. **5** I saw someone climbing over the wall. **6** Viktor heard his colleague arguing with the boss.

4

1 a **2** b **3** b **4** a **5** b **6** a **7** a **8** b **9** a **10** b **11** a **12** b **13** b **14** a

Review and consolidation unit 4

Futures (1)

1

1 b **2** a **3** b **4** a **5** a **6** a

Future Perfect and Future Continuous

2

1 will have cleaned **2** you will be sunbathing **3** Will you be watching
4 will have repaired **5** will have travelled **6** Will you have finished
7 Will you be visiting **8** will be asking

Verb patterns: -ing forms and infinitives

3

1 to take **2** to help **3** eating **4** to meet **5** cleaning **6** speaking
7 to use **8** feeling **9** drinking **10** to lock

4

1 a **2** b **3** a **4** a **5** b **6** a

Personality traits for jobs

5

```
¹P  E  ²O  P  ³L  E
A      U      A
T      T      ⁴B  E  S  T
H      O
   ⁵F  I  G  U  R  E  S
   N      ⁶R                     ⁷D
   I      R              ⁸L      E
⁹P    ¹⁰T  E  A  M  ¹¹A  ¹²T  I  G  H  T
R      I         T      S.       A
E      A      ¹³C  T      T       I
S      T      H  I      E       L
¹⁴S  A  T  I  S  F  A  C  T  I  O  N
U      V      N  U      E       E
R      E      N  G      U       R
E            E  E
```

Work

6

1 voluntary **2** workaholic **3** commuting **4** workplace **5** paid
6 work-centred **7** home **8** a flexible

Verb phrases about time

7

1 b **2** c **3** a **4** c **5** b **6** c

Collocations with prepositions

8

I think one of the most important things in life is being happy at work. I'm a website designer and I remember that when I applied ~~to~~ **for** my current job, I told the interviewer I wasn't just keen ~~of~~ **on** design, I was passionate ~~on~~ **about** it! Perhaps that's one of the reasons I got the job. I suppose I'm quite lucky because not only do I love my work, I also get on really well with my colleagues. They are all very different ~~at~~ **from** me, but we all believe ~~to~~ **in** what we are doing, so there's a great team spirit in the office. I work for a big advertising agency. It's a very busy and competitive business. Some of my colleagues worry ~~of~~ **about** that but I just get on and do my work. I think I'm pretty good ~~of~~ **at** what I do and I'm really proud ~~in~~ **of** some of the work I've done for the company.

How to…

9

1 about **2** sure **3** possibility **4** Believe **5** do **6** fact

Unit 5 Risk

Lesson 5.1

Reading

1a

3

1b

1 F **2** T **3** F **4** T **5** F **6** F **7** T **8** T

1c

1 breaking news **2** news junkie **3** sifting through **4** fanatical obsession **5** stems from **6** a 'must-see' resource **7** inside stories
8 dead-end jobs **9** sprung up **10** juiciest gossip

Grammar | conditional structures (1)

2

1 If I get a laptop, I'll be able to send emails when I'm travelling.
2 If the train comes on time, I won't be late for my interview.
3 If Maribel passes the driving test, she'll buy a car.
4 If I lived near a pool, I'd swim more.
5 If Terry wasn't/weren't scared of flying, he would travel around the world.
6 If Celia could sing, she would join a choir.
7 If Dave hadn't known all the answers, he wouldn't have won.
8 If Helena hadn't lost the tickets, she would have gone to the concert.
9 If Malik's sales figures hadn't been disappointing, he might have got a promotion.
10 If we hadn't had to queue up for tickets, we wouldn't have missed the start of the show.
11 If he had got good marks in his exams, Malcolm would be at university now.
12 If my parents were rich they would have bought me expensive presents.

3

1 would/'d like **2** wouldn't have happened **3** had/'d been **4** would have told **5** phone/phoned **6** will/'ll be able / would be able
7 doesn't have **8** will not/won't know **9** finds **10** will/'ll contact

Lesson 5.2

Reading

1a

2

1b

1 Eight **2** tickets and a full schedule **3** Yes **4** 25 **5** £20

1c

1 turn fantasy into reality **2** leading **3** longing for **4** closely-guarded
5 thrilling **6** humdrum **7** predictable **8** instructors

Grammar | advice and permission

2

1 Could **2** shouldn't **3** were **4** allowed **5** have **6** aren't **7** should
8 wouldn't

3

(**suggested answers**) **1** You aren't allowed to take photos in here.
2 You shouldn't go so fast. **3** In those days, women couldn't wear trousers to work.
4 You should have brought a coat! **5** If I were you, I wouldn't wear shoes with such high heels. **6** We should buy sun cream – it's going to be hot this weekend.

Vocabulary | sport

4

1 helmet **2** training **3** competitive **4** lifejackets **5** rafting **6** gloves
7 in **8** spectators

Pronunciation | connected speech (3)

5b

1 /w/ **2** weak form **3** /r/ **4** weak form **5** /j/

Lesson 5.3

Listening

1a

2

1b

	Daniel Craig	Matt Damon	Pierce Brosnan	Sean Connery
has done his own stunts	✓	✓		
didn't do stunts			✓	✓
jumped off a building	✓			
did martial arts training		✓		
was in a James Bond movie	✓		✓	✓
is American		✓		

1c

1 martial arts **2** documentary **3** maimed **4** role **5** special effects
6 tougher **7** action sequences **8** fake

Grammar | emphasis

2

1 so **2** did **3** such **4** It **5** does

3

1 I do like your new suit. **2** Amanda does complain a lot. **3** He did say he was sorry several times. **4** I did ask the boss for permission.
5 We do know what we are talking about.

4

1 such **2** so **3** so **4** such **5** many **6** so **7** such **8** so

5

(**suggested answers**) **1** No, it's Chinese food they love. **2** No, it's his assistant she spoke to. **3** No, it's the first film I like. **4** No, it's my thumb that hurts. **5** No, it's modern poetry that Clara doesn't like.
6 No, it's his attitude I don't like.

Pronunciation | stress: emphasis (1)

6

1 The children <u>did</u> behave themselves. **2** She's <u>such</u> a lovely person.
3 We <u>do</u> love Hollywood movies. **4** That old computer is <u>so</u> slow.
5 It was <u>Jane</u> that wanted to see you.

Vocabulary | phrasal verbs with *out*

7a

1 find **2** run **3** turned **4** give **5** sort

7b

1 We weren't sure about the babysitter but she ~~took~~ **turned** out to be really good. **2** ✓ **3** My car broke down last week and the mechanic wasn't able to ~~put~~ **sort** it out. **4** ✓ **5** Make sure you ~~fall~~ **put** out your cigarettes before you enter the building. **6** If I have a problem with my house, my neighbour ~~turns~~ **sorts** it out – he's a builder.

How to... | talk about which film to watch

8

1 a hard time **2** Judging by **3** the sound of **4** based on **5** sounds a bit

Review and consolidation unit 5

Conditional structures (1)

1

1 c **2** b **3** b **4** a **5** b **6** a **7** c **8** b **9** c **10** a

Advice and permission

2

1 In the 19th century, women **weren't** allowed to become members of the British parliament. **2** If I were you, I wouldn't **have** wasted so much time on the Internet. **3** Excuse me. **Could/Can** I use your mobile phone to make a short call? Mine isn't working. **4** You **shouldn't** believe everything politicians say – they rarely tell the whole truth. **5** We were lucky. When we were young we **could** stay out all day playing in the fields around my grandmother's house. **6** I'm sorry but you aren't **allowed** to come in here unless you wear a jacket and tie. **7** Once you have provided us with a valid email address you **can** use our software free of charge. **8** Where are the potatoes? You **should've** bought some when you went shopping this morning.

Emphasis

3

1 It was the shellfish that made me feel sick. **2** She did try to contact you. **3** I do admire people who do voluntary work. **4** It is my left leg that is injured. **5** Gerald is such a good footballer. **6** She does give a lot of money to charity. **7** It was my mobile phone that was stolen.
8 Yesterday's football match was so exciting. **9** Javier did do a lot of work for us. **10** It is his wife that does the housework.

4

1 that **2** does **3** so **4** It **5** did **6** do **7** such **8** is

Risk and achievement

5

1 opportunity/chance **2** ambition **3** substantial **4** gamble **5** stake
6 chance/opportunity

Challenge and sport

6

1 j **2** k **3** i **4** h **5** l **6** d **7** f **8** b **9** c **10** e **11** g **12** a

Phrasal verbs with *out*

7

1 works out **2** put out **3** find out **4** run out **5** sort out **6** fell out

Distances and dimensions

8

1 LENGTHEN **2** HEIGHTEN **3** LOW **4** WIDE **5** HEIGHT **6** HIGH
7 BREADTH **8** DEEP **9** BROADEN

How to...

9

1 make **2** Judging **3** hard **4** finish **5** sound

Unit 6 The past

Lesson 6.1

Listening

1a

(**suggested answers**) **1** Joe made TV commercials and short films.
2 A lot of money is involved. **3** There isn't much contact with accountants. **4** The distances are enormous so you have to drive to the shops. **5** They'd usually walk to do their shopping.
6 Sunny weather.

1b

1 How long has Joe been in the US? **2** How old was he when he came to the US? **3** Why did he choose to live in the States? **4** How many films has Joe made in the US? **5** What is different about film-making in the US? **6** What does his wife miss? **7** Why do people have to drive everywhere/to the shops? **8** Why didn't they do much filming outdoors in England?

1c

1 melting pot **2** studio executives **3** drive somebody mad
4 to be on top of somebody **5** location work

Grammar | *used to/would*

2
1 used to **2** would/'d / used to **3** would /'d/ used to **4** didn't use to
5 getting used to **6** would/'d **7** didn't use to **8** am/'m used to

3
1 a, c **2** a, c **3** a, b, c **4** b **5** a, c **6** b, c **7** b, c **8** a, b **9** b **10** b

Vocabulary | appearance

4

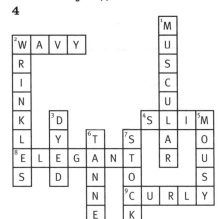

Pronunciation | consonant clusters (1)

5a
1 squash **2** stocky **3** splash **4** sphere **5** spiky **6** snow

Lesson 6.2

Reading

1a
3

1b
1 d **2** k **3** l **4** g **5** a **6** i **7** e **8** b **9** j **10** c **11** f **12** h

1c
1 convertible **2** set off **3** rushing **4** sprawled **5** groaning
6 spending spree **7** flag (it) down **8** exhausted **9** lent
10 removal truck

Grammar | wishes and regrets

2
1 I wish I'd gone to university. **2** I was going to buy an extra copy (but they had sold out). **3** If Ali had brought his computer he could have read his emails. **4** If only I'd spent more time studying. **5** If we'd liked the hotel we would've enjoyed our stay. **6** I regret leaving/that I left the party so early. **7** I was going to stay there longer (but my visa ran out). **8** I regret not paying more attention to my tutor's advice.

How to... | reminisce about the past

4
1 They went to the seaside in summer, not winter. **2** They had picnics on the beach, not in the forest. **3** There are two sisters, not three.
4 They are serving food to the father, not the other way around.

Lesson 6.3

Vocabulary | feelings

1
1 relieved **2** curious **3** confused **4** excited **5** annoyed **6** suspicious
7 shocked **8** sceptical

2
1 uninterested **2** excited **3** optimistic **4** uneasy **5** suspicious
6 relieved

Reading

3a
1 c **2** e **3** b

3b
1 The local police. **2** The labels were missing. **3** Because there was a piano there. **4** Because he played the piano so well. **5** Because he may be from Eastern Europe. **6** Students' own answers.

3c
1 dubbed **2** con artist **3** amnesia **4** appealed **5** traumatic
6 disoriented **7** non-stop **8** wandering **9** virtuoso **10** chapel
11 circulated **12** immigrant

Grammar | preparatory *it*

4
1 no use **2** my intention **3** seems **4** clear **5** was exciting
6 was good **7** worth **8** was sad

5
1 It's no use ~~that~~ relying on him, he's not very trustworthy. **2** ✓
3 It ~~important is~~ **is important** not to tell anyone your credit card PIN number. **4** It's always good to ~~getting~~ **get** a second opinion when you want to buy something expensive. **5** ✓ **6** ✓ **7** It ~~a real pleasure was~~ **was a real pleasure** to meet your parents at last. **8** It was strange ~~that~~ to see so many new faces at the youth club.

Review and consolidation unit 6

used to/would

1
1 Are you getting used to life in the big city? **2** Sally didn't use to have any friends when she was a child. **3** I would go to the library every morning when I was a student. **4** The company used to export cars to Asia. **5** Did he get used to the software quickly? **6** When I was young I didn't use to watch much television. **7** How often would you get the bus to school? **8** I've got used to staying up late. **9** It was easy to get used to the computer. **10** Pepe didn't use to live in a big house.

Wishes and regrets

2
1 I was going to send Maria a birthday card ... **2** If only I hadn't woken up late ... **3** I wish I'd ... **4** If I hadn't had a headache, I would've ...
5 I regret not studying psychology ... **6** ... would've liked to be a vet.

Preparatory *it*

3
(**suggested answers**) **1** seeing **2** to **3** it **4** It's **5** that **6** it's **7** to
8 having

Memory

4
1 b **2** a **3** b **4** c **5** a **6** b

Appearance

5
1 clean-shaven **2** wrinkles **3** bald **4** wavy/curly **5** muscular
6 scruffy **7** mousy **8** good-looking **9** dyed **10** round

Feelings

6
1 UNINTERESTED **2** SCEPTICAL **3** CONFUSED **4** ANNOYED
5 OPTIMISTIC **6** RELIEVED **7** CURIOUS **8** SHOCKED **9** EXCITED
10 UNEASY

Idioms to describe people

7
1 of → in **2** ~~position~~ → place **3** ✓ **4** ~~a nail~~ → nails
5 ~~know everything~~ → know-all **6** ✓ **7** ~~high flying~~ → high-flyer
8 ~~awkward custom~~ → awkward customer

How to...

8
1 as **2** in order to **3** to **4** so that **5** because

Unit 7 Excess

Lesson 7.1

Listening

1a
1 Three **2** Which take-away restaurant to go to/What to eat.
3 To go to the Chinese take-away.

1b
1 A **2** B **3** T **4** A **5** B **6** A **7** B **8** T

1c
Feeling very hungry: starving, ravenous, I could eat a horse
Positive opinion: yummy, delicious, scrumptious
Negative opinion: not too keen on, disgusting, greasy, to be sick of something, tasteless

Pronunciation | intonation: questions
2a
a 1, 2, 5 **b** 3, 4

Grammar | quantifiers
3
1 c 2 b 3 a 4 c 5 b 6 a 7 a 8 c 9 a 10 c
4
1 a, b 2 a, b 3 a 4 b 5 a 6 a, b

Vocabulary | food and cooking
5
1 grated cheese 2 electric cooker 3 grilled sausages
4 scrambled eggs 5 talented cook 6 sour milk

How to... | give and check instructions
6
A: ~~The first~~ **First**, you break two or three eggs into a cup and whisk them up. Grate some cheese and add it to the eggs. ~~Finally~~ **Then**, you heat up some butter in a frying pan. You must ~~do~~ **make** sure the butter's nice and hot. Then you pour the egg mix into the pan.
B: So, you mean ~~it~~ you mix the cheese in with the eggs before you put them in the pan?
A: Yes, but you can also add more cheese later.
B: OK.
A: Then you leave the egg and cheese mixture to cook for a few seconds. But you should ~~careful be~~ **be careful** not to let it get too hot.
B: Is **it** because it can burn?

Lesson 7.2

Reading
1a
2
1b
1 d 2 f 3 a 4 g 5 c 6 b 7 h 8 e
1c
1 valuable 2 argue 3 rival 4 follow his lead 5 impact
6 masterpieces 7 recession 8 wholly

Vocabulary | verb phrases about shopping
2
1 ~~refund~~ → receipt 2 ~~bargain~~ → discount 3 ~~haggling~~ → bidding
4 ~~worth~~ → afford 5 ~~bidding~~ → haggling 6 ~~afford~~ → worth

Grammar | passives
3
1 was created 2 was taken over 3 had started 4 scored
5 organised 6 were/had been sold 7 were invited 8 was bought
4
2 The metal strips are fed into a cutting machine. 3 The metal is cut into round shapes called 'blanks'. 4 After they have been cut out the blanks are heated in a furnace. 5 The blanks are washed while they are being heated./While they are being heated the blanks are washed.
6 each coin is stamped with a pattern on both sides. 7 The coins are cooled and counted. 8 The coins are distributed to the banks.
5
2 The present mustn't be opened until your birthday. 3 The crime is being investigated. 4 The hotel is going to be opened in November.
5 The children will be driven to the party. 6 My house can be seen from the top of the hill. 7 They were being watched. 8 That DVD hasn't been released yet. 9 The burglar might have been seen.
10 Nothing was taken.

How to... | complain about goods and services
6
a about b sorry c faulty d offer e replacement f grateful
g promise h do

Pronunciation | stress: emphasis (2)
7b
1 I'm <u>terribly</u> sorry about that. 2 But <u>what</u> are you going to do about it?
3 I <u>really</u> need to have a reliable Internet connection. 4 I <u>do</u> apologise for any inconvenience.

Lesson 7.3

Listening
1a
1 goldfish 2 dog 3 snake 4 horse 5 cats
1b
1 dog 2 horse 3 fish 4 dog 5 horse 6 cats 7 snake 8 horse
1c
Ways animals move: trot, dart, crawl
Places animals live: tank, stable, kennel
Animal characteristics: sinuous, playful, gentle

Grammar | *have/get something done*
2
1 has her hair done 2 has his car washed 3 have their house painted
4 has her eyes tested 5 has his blood pressure checked
6 have our boiler serviced
3
1 The bag got left behind. 2 Linda has her clothes washed (by the maid). 3 I have my post forwarded (to me). 4 Will you get your hair cut this week? 5 How often do you have your windows cleaned?
6 I should get/have my homework done by six o'clock.

Vocabulary | excess
4
1 OVERPRICED 2 EXTRAVAGANT 3 NECESSITY 4 LUXURY
5 EXCESSIVE 5 EXTRA 6 GOURMET 7 TREAT 8 INDULGE 9 LAVISH
10 SPOILT 11 FETCHED 12 SPREE 13 SPOIL 14 TOP 15 PAMPER

Review and consolidation unit 7

Passives
1
1 has been debited from your credit card. 2 is used for your security.
3 is being sent by email. 4 will not be sent by post. 5 must be brought to check-in one hour before departure. 6 cannot be changed. 7 can be pre-booked on the website. 8 is not allowed on any GoAway Travel flights. 9 may be purchased on the plane. 10 are included in the price.

Quantifiers
2
1 ~~luggages~~ luggage 2 ✓ 3 ~~many~~ much 4 ~~little~~ a little 5 ~~a lots~~ a lot / lots 6 ~~a few~~ a little 7 ✓ 8 ~~a spaghetti~~ spaghetti / some spaghetti
9 ~~few~~ a few 10 ~~much~~ many

have/get something done
3
1 had 2 got/been 3 (dry-)cleaned 4 have/get 5 repaired/fixed/mended 6 got/was 7 done 8 taken/printed/copied

How to...
4
1 b 2 e 3 h 4 a 5 g 6 d 7 f 8 c

Food and cooking
5
1 VEGETABLES 2 RAW 3 BITTER 4 SAUCEPAN 5 BEAT
6 SCRAMBLE 7 VEGETARIAN 8 RARE 9 RECIPE 10 GRATE 11 SLICE
12 SALTY 13 CABBAGE 14 PEACH 15 SWEET

Excess
6
1 luxury 2 extravagant 3 far-fetched 4 spending 5 overpriced
6 extra-large

Verb phrases about shopping
7
1 bargain 2 afford 3 haggling 4 receipt 5 bidding 6 discount
7 worth 8 refund

Prefixes

8
1 reheat **2** multinational **3** extra-large **4** uncomfortable
5 bilingual **6** overtired **7** ex-boyfriend **8** monotonous
9 undercooked **10** multipurpose

Unit 8 Success

Lesson 8.1

Reading

1a
1 d **2** f **3** a **4** h **5** b **6** e
1b
1 F **2** T **3** T **4** T **5** F **6** T **7** F **8** T
1c
1869: born in Porbandar, western India
1893: qualified as a lawyer
1915 : returned to India, determined to fight against colonialism
1947: India gained independence
1948: assassinated by a Hindu fanatic

Grammar | *It's time/I'd rather/I'd better*

2
1 a **2** b **3** b **4** b **5** b **6** a **7** a **8** a
3
1 It's time you moved to a bigger flat. **2** You'd better take an umbrella. **3** I'd rather go to the cinema. **4** It's time John got a better computer. **5** Would you like me to bring my camera / Would you rather I brought my camera? **6** I'd rather she didn't smoke. **7** I'd rather not work at the weekend. **8** You'd better have the salad.

Vocabulary | describing people

4
1 MANIPULATIVE **2** INTROVERTED **3** OPINIONATED **4** AGGRESSIVE
5 EASY **6** SELFISH **7** HEADSTRONG **8** OPEN **9** PROACTIVE
10 WITTY **11** MINDED

How to... | introduce general and specific points

5
1 Generally **2** rule **3** the time **4** especially **5** Suddenly
6 actually feel

Lesson 8.2

Listening

1a
1 They are in a gym. **2** She is a trainer/fitness instructor.
3 To get fit, lose weight and improve his energy levels.
1b
1 six **2** five **3** awfully **4** still **5** feels **6** energy **7** lethargic/tired
8 nutrition
1c
1 feeling lethargic **2** slave driver **3** get fit **4** catching up
5 be positive **6** cut out

Vocabulary | adjectives and intensifiers

2
1 absolutely **2** very **3** very **4** absolutely **5** absolutely **6** very
7 absolutely **8** very

Grammar | reported speech

3
1 he was still finding it quite difficult. **2** (that) it usually takes about three months to get fit. **3** if he had cut out all those sweet snacks. **4** he would give it a try. **5** if she had prepared that nutrition sheet for him.
4
1 c **2** f **3** a **4** h **5** b **6** g **7** e **8** d
5
1 c **2** a **3** b **4** b **5** c **6** b **7** a **8** b **9** b **10** c

Pronunciation | intonation: reporting

6a
Higher intonation: direct speech
Lower intonation: reported speech

Lesson 8.3

Reading

1a
1 e **2** b **3** a **4** c **5** d
1b
1 later this month next month **2** exam practical **3** five nine **4** maths computer **5** son daughter **6** The parents decide Ryde decides
7 older younger **8** few most
1c
1 e **2** h **3** b **4** j **5** a **6** d **7** i **8** f **9** c **10** g

How to... | report the results of a survey

2
1 out of **2** vast **3** of **4** everyone **5** Nearly **6** Most **7** small
8 majority **9** No one

Grammar | reporting verbs

3
1 e **2** a **3** f **4** b **5** d **6** c
4
1 My brother suggested going out for a meal. **2** John explained that he couldn't come because he had to work that evening. **3** The children denied taking it/that they had taken it. **4** The lifeguard warned (us) that swimming after eating can/could be dangerous. **5** Maria admitted that the reason she had failed the exam was because she didn't do/hadn't done her homework. **6** The sales representative confirmed (that) they can/could deliver the parcel tomorrow/the next day.

Review and consolidation unit 8

It's time/I'd rather/I'd better

1
1 time **2** rather **3** It's **4** better **5** would/'d **6** phoned/called/rang
7 had/'d **8** Would **9** not **10** be

Reported speech

2
1 (that) she had tried his mobile. **2** (him) if he was out playing football that day. **3** (that) she was phoning because she needed some advice. **4** him (that) her landlord had asked her to leave.
5 (that) he/the landlord wanted her to go at the end of that/the month. **6** (that) she was very worried about it. **7** if he/Steve could give her any advice. **8** him (that) she would be at home all day the next day.

Reporting verbs

3
(suggested answers)
1 [c] (that) the doctor was sick that day so he couldn't see me.
2 [e] to do all the exercises on page 65 of the Workbook. **3** [h] (that) we go/going to the cinema on Friday evening. **4** [a] not to touch those plates because they were very hot. **5** [i] had stolen the money.
6 [b] where my passport was. **7** [g] if/whether I was feeling alright. **8** [f] (that) I would have to get a new hard drive for my laptop. **9** [d] to be at the airport two hours before our departure. **10** [j] (that) they had copied/copying their homework from the Internet.

Success

4
1 b **2** d **3** f **4** a **5** c **6** g **7** h **8** e

Describing personality

5
1 single-minded **2** headstrong **3** outgoing **4** manipulative **5** witty
6 introverted **7** proactive **8** aggressive **9** selfish **10** opinionated

Adjectives/intensifiers

6
1 upset **2** clean **3** tiny **4** ✓ **5** fascinating **6** ✓ **7** happy **8** freezing

Phrasal verbs with three parts

7
1 look; to **2** cut; on **3** looking; to **4** put; with **5** come; with
6 get; with **7** made; for **8** catch; with

8
1 out of **2** On the whole **3** vast **4** a rule **5** minority **6** nearly

Unit 9 Crime

Lesson 9.1

Vocabulary | law and insurance

1a
1 convicted → sentenced **2** fraud → arson **3** sentenced → sued
4 premium → fraud **5** sued → convicted **6** insure → commit
7 arson → premium **8** commit → insure

1b
1 of **2** for **3** to **4** with

Reading

2a
1 f **2** d **3** c

2b
1 What does cruise control do? **2** Why did Mr Grazinski step into the back of the motor home? **3** What injuries did he suffer from? **4** Why did Kara Walton climb through the window of the ladies toilet? **5** How much compensation was she awarded? **6** How long had Terrence Dickson's career as a burglar lasted? **7** Why was he trapped in the garage for eight days? **8** What did he live on while he was trapped in the garage?

2c
Vehicles: cruise control, accelerator, speed, mph, owner's manual
Injuries/Harm: suffered, fell, broke, knocked out, starvation
Legal: court, awarded, compensation, expenses, jury

Grammar | participle clauses for sequencing

3
1 A few days after buying the motor home ... **2** Having joined the motorway, he set the cruise control at 65 mph and decided to step into the back of the motor home to make himself a cup of coffee. **3** ... while struggling to get through the window, she fell to the floor and knocked out her two front teeth. **4** After entering the garage from the house, he realised the door could not be opened from the inside.

4
1 a **2** b **3** a **4** a **5** b **6** a

5
(suggested answers) 1 Having told his best friend, Dave announced the news to his colleagues. **2** After getting up, he went into the village to get some food. **3** They watched the midnight movie before going to bed. / Before going to bed, they watched the midnight movie. **4** While (she was) watching TV Surinda heard a strange sound. / Surinda heard a strange sound while she was watching TV. **5** We went to the computer shop after reading lots of consumer reports. / After reading lots of consumer reports, we went to the computer shop. **6** Having missed the bus, Jackie had to get a taxi. **7** My uncle started a new business after he had gone to America. / Having gone to America, my uncle started a new business. **8** The kids usually watch TV for an hour after doing their homework. / After doing their homework, the kids usually watch TV for an hour.

Pronunciation | consonant clusters (2)

6a
1 against **2** products **3** suspects **4** insurance **5** punishments **6** clients

Lesson 9.2

Listening

1a
1 b **2** c **3** c **4** a **5** a

1b
1 download **2** unravel **3** on behalf of **4** proportion **5** sort of **6** look like

1c
1 on behalf of **2** look like **3** download **4** sort of **5** unravel **6** proportion

Grammar | deduction: present and past

2
1 f **2** a **3** g **4** h **5** e **6** c **7** d **8** b

3
1 He must be at home. **2** They can't/couldn't have left the country. **3** It might need a service. **4** They must have left already. **5** She can't be guilty. **6** She might not have received the invitation. **7** You must have forgotten to bring it. **8** The battery might be flat.

4
1 must have **2** can't **3** must have **4** must **5** can't have **6** might

Vocabulary | compound adjectives

5
1 middle-aged **2** fire-proof **3** well-dressed **4** red-handed **5** tongue-tied

Pronunciation | compound adjectives

6
1 Mr Lockwood is middle-aged. **2** Wooden buildings are dangerous because they aren't fire-proof. **3** When you go to a job interview you should be well-dressed. **4** The thief was caught red-handed. **5** When I meet new people I am often tongue-tied.

Lesson 9.3

Reading

1a
3

1b
1 T **2** T **3** T **4** F **5** F **6** T **7** T **8** F

1c
1 g **2** d **3** a **4** e **5** h **6** c **7** b **8** f

Grammar | relative clauses

2
1 a **2** b **3** b **4** a **5** a **6** b **7** a **8** b

3
1 who **2** that/which **3** 23, was **4** you/that you **5** where **6** which **7** that sold **8** who/that

4
1 Miranda's boyfriend, who lives in Athens, is a doctor. **2** The house (that) I'm living in is over a hundred years old. **3** Arthur Conan Doyle, who was Scottish, was born in 1859. **4** The government, which was elected last year, has introduced a new tax. **5** Our local hospital, which is very old, is about to be closed down. **6** The girl (who/that) we met on holiday is coming to stay next weekend. **7** Spielberg's new film, which I saw yesterday, was fantastic. **8** The hotel (that) we stayed in last summer had a heated swimming pool.

How to... | start, move on and finish a discussion

5
1 have **2** individually **3** start **4** for **5** on **6** come **7** like **8** agreed **9** What **10** think

Review and consolidation unit 9

Participle clauses

1
1 leaving **2** seen **3** On **4** After **5** ran **6** booking **7** living **8** Having **9** finishing **10** learned

Deduction: present and past

2
1 j **2** a **3** d **4** c **5** l **6** b **7** f **8** g **9** e **10** h

Relative clauses

3
1 My brother, who works in Cardiff, is an opera singer. **2** Jenny, who/whom I told you about, is getting married. **3** ✓ **4** The children that/who didn't pass the test had to retake it. **5** Our car, which we bought last year, has been stolen from our garage. **6** The film that was on TV last night was absolutely fascinating. **7** ✓ **8** My husband, who you met last week, has been promoted to the Los Angeles office.

4
1 It belonged to an old lady who died. **2** When I was young the old lady, who used to be a schoolteacher, allowed me to play in her garden. **3** The garden, which was huge, had lots of lemon trees. **4** I used to pick the lemons from the trees that grew there. **5** The old lady used the lemons (that) I had picked to make lemonade.

How to...

5

1 believe **2** individually **3** tell **4** to **5** Can **6** on

Crime, law and insurance

6

1 ARSON **2** FINGERPRINTS **3** CLAIM **4** SENTENCE **5** WITNESS
6 SUSPENDED **7** ROBBERY **8** CONVICT **9** ARRESTED **10** FORENSIC
11 PREMIUM **12** INNOCENT **13** SUE **14** EVIDENCE **15** PETTY
16 THIEF **17** VICTIM **18** FINE **19** FRAUD

Compound adjectives

7

1 c **2** h **3** a **4** f **5** g **6** b **7** e **8** d

News headlines

8

1 F **2** T **3** T **4** T **5** F **6** T **7** F **8** F

Unit 10 Mind

Lesson 10.1

Listening

1a

2

1b

1 Germany **2** qualified **3** Vienna **4** magnetism **5** Paris **6** aristocrats
7 king **8** entertained **9** forced **10** 1815

1c

1 a **2** d **3** a **4** d **5** c **6** b **7** b **8** c

Grammar | reflexive pronouns

2

1 b **2** c **3** a **4** c **5** a **6** c **7** a **8** c **9** a **10** b

3

1 Darren cut himself while he was gardening. **2** I made the cake myself. **3** We've made all the arrangements ourselves. **4** Mandy and Sylvia sent text messages to each other. **5** My central heating turns itself on automatically if the temperature drops. **6** The Bensons often send packages to themselves when they are abroad. **7** Did you paint this picture yourself? **8** Isabel works for herself.

Pronunciation | stress: reflexive pronouns

4a

1 it<u>self</u> **2** them<u>selves</u> **3** my<u>self</u> **4** him<u>self</u>

How to... | talk about beliefs and opinions

5

1 that → of **2** sceptic → sceptical **3** is reckons → reckons
4 convenienced → convinced **5** of → that **6** give → giving
7 it that → that **8** doubt → doubts

Lesson 10.2

Reading

1a

2

1b

1 F **2** F **3** T **4** F **5** T **6** T **7** F **8** F

1c

1 freshly baked **2** optimistic **3** pick up **4** cash register **5** subtly
6 olfactory organs **7** evocative **8** harness

Vocabulary | advertising

2

1 slogan **2** brands **3** target market

Grammar | conditional structures (2): with conjunctions

3

1 fail the exam, what will you do? **2** water them, palm trees won't grow in Sweden. **3** pass the entrance test, we'll give you a place on the course. **4** unless you have a written invitation. **5** unless there is a power failure. **6** you pay by credit card, we will give you a guarantee. **7** the neighbours complain, you can have a party. **8** you show us a receipt we can give you a refund.

4

1 went → 'll go **2** can't → can **3** did → will **4** As long that → As long as
5 don't have → have **6** would → wouldn't **7** stay → will stay
8 would supply → supply

How to... | persuade someone to do something

5

1 sure **2** Come **3** fun **4** supposing **5** lose **6** just **7** treat
8 deserve **9** regret **10** go

Pronunciation | intonation: sounding enthusiastic

6

1 <u>Come</u> on, I'm <u>sure</u> it'll be fun. **2** What have you got to <u>lose</u>?
3 Let's <u>treat</u> ourselves. **4** <u>Come</u> on, I'm <u>sure</u> you won't regret it.
5 OK, let's <u>go</u> for it then.

Lesson 10.3

Reading

1a

False

1b

1 D **2** M **3** C/H **4** M **5** H **6** D/M **7** H **8** C

1c

1 geek **2** hypocrites **3** immoral **4** fuss **5** miniature
6 nightmare

Vocabulary | verb phrases with *mind*

2

1 speak my mind. **2** slipped my mind. **3** make up your mind / make your mind up. **4** sprang to mind **5** changed her mind
6 keep my mind on **7** crossed your mind **8** keep it in mind

Grammar | futures (2)

3

1 If **2** will **3** could **4** comes **5** going to **6** intending

4

1 a **2** a **3** b **4** b **5** b **6** a **7** b **8** a

5

1 'll have **2** you're sitting **3** could **4** I've decided **5** don't
6 going to be

Review and consolidation unit 10

Reflexive pronouns

1

1 her → herself **2** himself → him **3** others → other **4** ✓
5 ourself → ourselves **6** themselves → them **7** ✓
8 repaired me → repaired the broken chair myself

Conditional structures (2): with conjunctions

2

1 b **2** c **3** b **4** a **5** c **6** b **7** a **8** c **9** c **10** b

Futures (2)

3

1 I've decided **2** going to talk **3** agrees **4** is going to
5 determined **6** could **7** I'd **8** didn't **9** I'm taking **10** I'll finish

The power of the mind

4

1 unconscious **2** déjà vu **3** trust **4** premonition **5** mind
6 willpower **7** subconscious **8** persuasion

Advertising

5

1 TRAILER **2** SLOGAN **3** LOGO **4** COMMERCIAL **5** MARKET
6 MARKETING **7** HYPE **8** BRAND **9** ADVERTISEMENT

Verb phrases with *mind*

6

1 d **2** a **3** e **4** f **5** c **6** b

Commonly misspelt words

7

1 intelligence **2** psychologist **3** subconscious **4** their **5** responsibility
6 definitely **7** changeable **8** necessary **9** generous **10** occasionally

How to...

8

1 I am convinced that Jimmy is guilty of the crime. **2** Emily is in favour
of longer prison sentences for criminals. **3** I think you should go for it.
4 I've always believed that people are basically honest. **5** I'm sure it'll
be fun! **6** I'm sceptical about hypnosis.

Pearson Education Limited
Edinburgh Gate
Harlow
Essex CM20 2JE
England
and Associated Companies throughout the world.

www.pearsonelt.com

First published 2011
Fifth impression 2013

ISBNs:
9781408267417
New Total English Upper Intermediate Workbook (with Key) and
Audio CD Pack
9781408267424
New Total English Upper Intermediate Workbook (without Key) and
Audio CD Pack

Set in MetaPlusBook-Roman
Printed in Slovakia by Neografia

Design: Pearson Education

Photo acknowledgements

The publisher would like to thank the following for their kind
permission to reproduce their photographs:

(Key: b-bottom; c-centre; l-left; r-right; t-top)

Alamy Images: Fancy 62, Photo Japan 9; **Corbis:** Mike Gunnill /
epa 48, Jacques Langevin / Sygma 54, Ron Sachs / CNP 36, Ariel
Skelley 47; **Fotolia.com:** pressmaster 77, tomalu 7; **Getty Images:**
Hulton Archive 60; **Sally and Richard Greenhill:** Sally and Richard
Greenhill 22; **iStockphoto:** Christian Waldegger 38t; **Pearson
Education Ltd:** Corbis 32l, Image Source Ltd. www.imagesource.
com 12, Imagestate. John Foxx Collection 56, Photodisc. Karl
Weatherly 38b; **Photolibrary.com:** Hank De Lespinasse 17, Digital
Nation 16, kihiro Sugimoto 32r; **Rex Features:** Greg Allen 18,
c.20thC.Fox / Everett 72, c.Col Pics / Everett 44, c.MGM / Everett
40, IPC Magazines / Chat 37, Ken McKay 4; **TopFoto:** TopFoto.co.uk /
Ray Roberts 30; **www.delfly.nl:** 80; **www.icehotel.com:** 14

Cover images: *Front:* **Alamy Images:** Maros Markovic

All other images © Pearson Education

Every effort has been made to trace the copyright holders and we
apologise in advance for any unintentional omissions. We would
be pleased to insert the appropriate acknowledgement in any
subsequent edition of this publication.